'You're just like every other man—you just want to be the centre of attention. Well, this time you definitely come second!'

They stood there, glaring at each other in the suddenly shattering silence. Then Sebastian, his voice glacial, said through gritted teeth, 'Well, thank you very much. At least I know where I stand.' And he turned on his heel and strode away, slamming the door behind him.

Verity slumped against the half-stripped wall, realising that she'd driven him away.

# LORD OF MISRULE

BY
SALLY WENTWORTH

**MILLS & BOON LIMITED**
ETON HOUSE    18-24 PARADISE ROAD
RICHMOND    SURREY    TW9 1SR

*First published in Great Britain 1990
by Mills & Boon Limited*

© Sally Wentworth 1990

*Australian copyright 1990
Philippine copyright 1990
This edition 1990*

ISBN 0 263 76662 4

*Set in Times Roman 10½ on 12 pt.
01-9004-52731 C*

*Made and printed in Great Britain*

# CHAPTER ONE

HEATHROW AIRPORT was as busy and noisy as always. Verity Mitchell stopped to let a harassed woman pushing a loaded trolley go past, and then weaved her way through the throng until she stood in front of the Arrivals board. Her eyes ran down the list until she reached flight number BA32 from Bahrain. The expected arrival time was slightly ahead of schedule. Verity glanced at her watch and gave a little nod of satisfaction; allowing for the plane to land, and Paula to collect her luggage and get through Customs, she probably had only about half an hour to wait. Time for a coffee, anyway.

It was quieter in the coffee shop and she was served quickly, but Verity was unable to relax as she drank it; she kept remembering the last time she'd been at Heathrow, when she had returned from Bahrain after supporting Paula through her husband's funeral. It had been an extremely harrowing time and Verity had felt terrible about leaving her friend behind, but now Paula was coming home at last. Restlessly, Verity glanced at her watch—still another quarter of an hour to wait. But then it occurred to her that Paula was pregnant and the airport authorities might have given her a ride from the plane in one of their motorised conveyors. That thought made her hurriedly finish her coffee and walk briskly down the stairs to the narrow exit where arriving travellers emerged into the main concourse.

There was the usual crowd of waiting people pressing against the barriers, some holding up placards with names printed on them. Verity found a space and stood as patiently as she could, her eyes on the emerging passengers. A plane must have come in; a small crowd of people came through and Verity leaned forward eagerly, but Paula wasn't among them. Then there was a short gap before some Arabs in robes and white head-dresses walked by, to be met by a uniformed chauffeur holding a placard with the indecipherable curves of Arabic writing. And there was Paula at last, looking as beautiful as ever and wearing a loose-fitting jacket that completely hid her pregnancy. She was walking along in her unhurried, elegant way beside a man who pushed a trolley piled high with cases—a man whom Verity didn't recognise. Verity waved and Paula waved back, the two girls rushing to hug one another as soon as Paula was clear of the barrier.

'Are you all right? You *look* great! Oh, Paula, I'm so glad you're back.'

'It's great to be here,' Paula smiled.

Verity looked at her anxiously. 'You're not too tired from the journey?'

'No, I'm fine.' But then Paula shivered. 'But it's so *cold* here.'

The man beside her laughed and Paula turned to him with one of her best smiles. 'Thank you so much for coming to my rescue; I'd never have been able to manage all that luggage myself. Verity, I met this kind man on the plane and he gallantly collected all my cases together for me.'

The stranger nodded to her and Verity smiled vaguely back, not in the least surprised; Paula had a deceptively fragile air that always brought people rushing to help her. 'My car's in the short-term car park. If you wouldn't mind...?' Verity had learned from experience to take full advantage of the muscle-power that Paula attracted.

So the cases were crammed into Verity's car and Paula's rescuer retrieved his one small holdall and waved them off, rewarded with a glowing smile from Paula.

They talked only of things that didn't matter during the drive to Verity's tiny terraced house in North London: of girls they had known at school, of films they had both seen and books they had recommended to each other and read. Luckily the house had a lock-up garage that took up most of the minute garden at the back, so they were able to drive the car in and leave all but one of Paula's suitcases inside. There seemed little point in lugging them all into the house when they would be leaving again in a couple of days. It wasn't until Paula had kicked off her shoes and was relaxing in the cosy sitting-room, the curtains drawn to shut out the world and the fire blazing to take off the chill, that she began to tell Verity of the weeks since the funeral.

'Everyone was so kind,' she murmured as she sipped a pre-dinner sherry. 'All our friends rallied round to help, winding up Simon's business affairs, and organising the sale of the bungalow and then the furniture.'

'It must have taken some time,' Verity remarked. 'It's been over four months.'

'Yes, it did take a while. But to be honest I wasn't in any great hurry to come back.'

Verity gave her a quick glance and then smiled. 'You never did like the English weather.'

'No.' Paula made no attempt to return the smile. 'But, as I told you when I phoned, I'm scared of going back to Simon's family home.'

'That's rather a strange word to use. Why should you be afraid?'

'I don't know.' Paula frowned and moved restlessly in her seat. 'I don't want to go there. I wish I hadn't inherited it.'

'But you haven't, have you? I mean, it will belong to the baby, not you.'

'Yes.' Paula instinctively put a hand on the growing roundness of her stomach. 'If I hadn't been pregnant the house would have gone to Simon's stepbrother, Sebastian Kent.'

'Oh, yes, I remember his mother—Simon's stepmother—came to Simon's funeral, didn't she? Wasn't her name Margaret Layton?'

Paula nodded. 'Yes, but she told me to call her Maggie.'

'She seemed all right. Quite nice, in fact,' Verity remarked.

'Yes—but at the time she didn't know I was pregnant. She thought that her son was going to inherit Simon's house.'

'Has her attitude changed, then?'

'She kept on at me to come back to England. As soon as I told her about the baby she kept writing and then phoning me. She said that the baby must be born at Layton House, that it was the family tradition.'

There was resentment in Paula's tone, but uncertainty too, and Verity realised that her friend was suffering from the problem that had dogged them both since their childhood—that they were orphans and had no parents or family to turn to for advice. They only had each other and the close friendship that had grown out of their loneliness and need to matter to someone.

'Traditions don't have to be kept up, you know,' Verity said lightly as she got to her feet. 'Come on, let's eat. I'm starving.'

She had made a casserole, which they ate in Verity's optimistically named dining-room, an area opening off the kitchen which was only just big enough to hold a pine table and four chairs as well as an old Welsh dresser that held her collection of antique teapots on its shelves.

After they'd eaten Paula immediately went to sit by the fire again. 'I hope it isn't going to be freezing cold all the time at Layton House,' she remarked fretfully. 'From what I've read, those big old houses in the country are always full of draughts.'

'Hasn't it got central heating?'

'I don't know. Simon never talked about the place very much. He was much more interested in setting up his business.'

'But his stepmother, Maggie, she always lived there and looked after it for him, didn't she?'

Paula nodded. 'Yes, with her son. That's why I'm sure she will resent me; it's far more their home than it could ever be mine.'

'Yes, it could be awkward,' Verity agreed. 'Especially if you decide to live there yourself and you want them to move out.'

'Exactly,' Paula sighed. 'And I can't even sell the place if I don't like it, because it will be in trust for the baby until he's twenty-one.'

'He?' Verity queried teasingly. 'I thought you were a feminist.'

'Pregnancy changes your attitude to life,' Paula answered. Her eyes shadowed. 'And so does bereavement. Oh, Verity, I miss Simon so. Physically, of course. And he always took care of everything. I really miss not having a man around to look after me. You don't know how wonderful that is.' She lifted her head to look at her friend. 'You *must* promise to come to Layton House with me. I can't possibly face it on my own.'

She began to cry a little and Verity quickly crossed the room and put her arm round her. 'You're tired after the flight. Why don't you go up and have a bath and go to bed? And I'll put a hot-water bottle in so that it will be warm for you.'

Paula agreed willingly enough, and within an hour was fast asleep in the spare room. Verity looked in on her before going to bed herself, and the next morning she moved quietly about the house until Paula came down at about eleven o'clock. She looked better, but then she always did look good, tiredness only shadowing her face so that she seemed more fragile. It was warmer today, the late September sun still with enough heat to make walking outside pleasant, but Paula was used to the equatorial temperatures of Bahrain and borrowed one of Verity's winter coats when they strolled down to the local pub for lunch and a drink.

The pub had an open area at the back, with so many flowering tubs and hanging baskets bright with winter-flowering pansies that you could almost believe you were in a garden.

'I'd almost forgotten what an English pub was like,' Paula said with a nostalgic smile. 'It must be more than two years since I was last in England.'

'Do you think you'll stay here now?'

'I suppose it depends on how things go at Layton House. But I must admit I'd like the baby to be born in England.'

'Well, if you don't like the place you don't have to live there. You can always come back to my house,' Verity pointed out.

Paula reached across the table and touched Verity's hand. 'I know,' she said gratefully. 'And don't think I won't. Although you might not be so eager to take me in if I have a crying baby to keep you awake at nights.'

'Nonsense,' Verity answered briskly. 'I shall enjoy being an adoptive aunt. It will be fun.'

'I'm so glad you're taking me down to Layton House. Will you be able to stay for a while?' Paula asked. 'Did you manage to persuade your company to let you have some time off?'

Verity shook her head. 'No, they wouldn't wear it. I'd already had two weeks off when I went over to Bahrain for the funeral, so I only had two more weeks' holiday due to me this year.'

'You can only stay for two weeks?' Paula exclaimed, a look of horror in her eyes. 'But I want you to stay with me at least until the baby is born.'

'No, it's OK; I quit the job. I can stay as long as you need me,' Verity reassured her.

'Oh, thank goodness. I couldn't stand being there without you, Verity. I just couldn't.'

'You'll probably love it,' Verity said hearteningly. 'Simon's family will welcome you with open arms,

and in two weeks you'll be so much at home that you'll
wonder what on earth you were worrying about.'

'I only wish it could be like that,' Paula said wist-
fully. 'But I just have this terrible feeling about the
place. Simon was never happy there, and I'm sure
that I'm going to hate it too. But with you there it
won't be anything like so lonely. I'll phone Maggie
up tonight and tell her you're definitely coming with
me.' She looked at Verity tensely. 'I'm sorry that you
had to leave your job; I know how much you loved
it.'

'For heaven's sake, it was only a job. There are
thousands of companies, probably far better, that are
just waiting to beg me to walk in and work for them,'
Verity answered lightly. 'And, besides, a holiday in
the country at this time of the year will be wonderful.
Just think of all the trees turning to gold and——'

'And the wind howling round the house and frost
on the windows,' Paula broke in.

They looked at each other and grinned, their deep
friendship ruling out any feelings of sacrifice or in-
debtedness. What Verity was doing for Paula would
have been done just as willingly the other way round.
They both knew that the friendship was the closest
and most trustworthy relationship they would ever
have, short of marriage, and that they could always
turn to each other in time of need. Even Paula's marriage to Simon and being so far apart had made no
difference; it had been Verity whom Paula had called
and wanted with her as soon as she'd heard of Simon's
death in a car crash.

In the afternoon they went shopping for warmer
clothes for Paula, and were unable to resist buying
several delightful outfits for the baby. 'They're so

tiny,' Verity marvelled. 'Are babies really as small as that?'

'I suppose so. I really don't know very much about babies or looking after them,' Paula admitted. 'I'll have to buy some books.'

'I thought it was all supposed to come naturally.'

'Maybe it does. I hope so. Sometimes the thought of giving birth and being responsible for another human being scares me to death.'

It wasn't the first remark of that nature that Paula had made. In the past she had always been very sure of herself and had sailed happily through life, her beauty and warmth giving her everything she wanted. But Simon's death had obviously shaken her very badly, leaving her nervous and vulnerable, and Verity realised that her own role during the next few weeks was not only going to be that of companion, but she would also have to try and boost Paula's self-confidence.

In the evening they went to a concert, and afterwards for a meal at an Italian restaurant, so there was no time for Paula to worry about what the next day might bring. And Verity deliberately forgot to set the alarm clock the next morning, so that they were both busy with last-minute jobs and packing, and it wasn't until they were in the car and on their way that Paula began to show signs of anxiety again.

'How long will it take us to get there, do you think?' she asked when they had only been driving for about half an hour.

'Well, at the rate my old car travels at the best of times, and loaded down with all this luggage, I should think we'll be lucky to get there at all,' Verity answered cheerfully. She glanced across at Paula. 'Stop worrying. Everything will be fine. If Maggie Layton and her son didn't want you at Layton House they would hardly have kept writing to ask you to come, now would they?'

'It was only Maggie who wrote and telephoned. I've never met her son.'

'But you must know something about him. Didn't Simon talk about him?'

'Not much. He only said that Sebastian was older, and an only child like himself.'

'But surely as stepbrothers they must have seen quite a lot of each other?'

Paula shook her head. 'No, I don't think so. Simon was sent away to school after his mother died, and he so loved to travel that he went on school trips abroad nearly every holiday and was seldom at home. Then, after he left university, he went to a business college in America for a couple of years, and after that started the company in Bahrain.'

'Which is where you met him,' Verity said when Paula fell silent. 'I'm surprised he never took you back to England to see the house after you were married.'

'There were so many other places to visit that I hadn't seen,' Paula answered with a shrug. 'We thought there would be plenty of time for going back to England.'

'So you really don't know very much about Sebastian.' Verity quickly reverted to their previous topic before Paula could get upset again.

'No. Simon said he was in business, but he was pretty vague about it.'

'And he didn't come to your wedding—or the funeral?'

'No. But then we got married so quietly that you were about the only person who came to the wedding.' Paula paused and then said heavily, 'And you know how quickly funerals take place in hot countries. Maggie said that Sebastian was abroad somewhere and she hadn't been able to notify him in time for him to come with her.'

'Well, that's quite possible. Stop worrying; he'll probably turn out to be very nice. Is he married?'

Paula shook her head. 'No, I don't think so.'

'In that case I was wrong, he'll probably turn out to be either a sports freak or a workaholic,' Verity said dolefully.

'Why on earth do you say that?' Paula asked in amazement.

'Because that's the only kind of unattached man I ever seem to meet nowadays. If they're not jetting off somewhere to pull off a business deal, then they're taking part in some sports tournament in a men-only club.'

Paula laughed delightedly, as she was meant to. 'I can see I'll have to take you under my wing. I quite fancy myself as a matchmaker.'

'Heaven forbid!' Verity exclaimed with a shudder. 'I still have nightmares about the last man you tried to pair me off with.'

They began to tease each other, and from there moved on to reminiscences about their adolescence, which kept them laughing for another fifty miles or so. But then the worst happened and the car spluttered to a halt and refused to start again. Verity had to walk over a mile to a phone, and then it took a couple of hours before the breakdown service came to tow them into a garage, and another hour before a new part was fitted. So, instead of arriving at Layton House in time for lunch as they'd intended, it was the afternoon when they drove down a tree-lined country lane and at last came to the entrance.

Verity stopped the car and they both looked across at the stone pillars supporting heavily ornate wrought-iron gates. On one pillar there was a copper plate deeply etched with the words 'Layton House'.

'I guess this is it,' Paula said nervously.

'Just how big is this house?' Verity asked uneasily.

'Simon just said it was big and old.'

'Hmm. Well, we're about to find out how big is big,' Verity murmured, and pulled across the road into the entrance. She was about to get out of the car to open the gates when a woman emerged from the little lodge to the left and hurried to do it for them. The girls gave her rather tight smiles of thanks and drove on. 'I suppose Simon didn't mention anything about employing any staff, did he?' Verity asked hollowly.

Paula shook her head, her eyes wide as she stared ahead, looking for the house.

They drove past a deep bank of rhododendrons, turned a corner, and both gasped. 'Oh, my God!' Paula exclaimed in an awestruck whisper.

'Quite.' Verity stopped the car again and they just sat and gazed at the house set on the other side of the shallow valley before them. It was a Georgian house, built of stone that had weathered to a mellow gold, but which shone like a jewel in the low autumn light, the sun reflecting from the many window-panes until the beauty of it hurt your eyes. Verity let out her breath on a long sigh. 'I've never seen such a lovely house.'

They turned to look at each other, Paula's eyes seeking reassurance, and Verity grinned at her. 'Welcome to the lady of the manor.'

It was the right thing to say. Paula turned to look at the house again with an arrested expression in her eyes. 'It is a manor, isn't it? I had no idea it would be so big.'

They gazed for a while longer, taking in the broad lawns in front of the house, which dropped down to a narrow river between steep banks that meandered along the bottom of the valley and disappeared into quite thick woodland at either side. Letting off the handbrake, Verity drove slowly forwards, across a cattle-grid that rattled under the wheels, and then across a stone bridge over the river and on to the sweeping curve in front of the house.

As they drew up, the big oak front door opened and Maggie Layton came hurrying out. 'So you made it at last! Thank goodness you rang to say you'd be late; I'd have been so worried about you. Paula, my dear, how are you?'

While the other two women greeted each other, Verity got out of the car and turned to look back over the gardens. From here she could see that the driveway branched off past the right-hand end of the house towards some stables, and then narrowed into a track that crossed the river again by a wooden bridge over-hung by a large chestnut tree. The sun filtered through the branches of the tree and dappled the ground, turning the leaves that had already fallen into a rich golden carpet. The colours and the faint sound of rushing water made an immediate appeal to Verity's imagination, and she decided to go and explore the track as soon as she was free to do so.

'Verity, how nice to see you again.'

She turned as Maggie Layton came towards her, hand outstretched in greeting. 'Hello, Mrs Layton. How are you?'

'Oh, call me Maggie, please. How annoying for you to break down like that. If Sebastian had been home I would have sent him to collect you and have your car sent on after it was mended, but unfortunately he's been away for the last few days and isn't due back until tonight. But do come in. I expect you're both dying for a cup of tea.' Verity went to reach into the car for the cases, but Maggie said, 'Oh, don't worry about those; I'll have them sent up to your rooms shortly.'

She led the way up the steps and through a wide hall into a very pleasant sitting-room. There was a big fireplace with logs that burnt brightly, chintz-covered settees, lovingly polished antique furniture, and paintings on the walls, but both girls' eyes swept the room, settled on one point, and then met in a flash of amused relief. The house was centrally heated; there was a wide radiator, discreetly hidden behind a latticed screen, beneath each window.

'Do make yourselves comfortable. I'll just go and get the tea; Mrs Chivers will probably have it ready by now.'

She went out of the room and Paula swung round. 'Wow! I can't take it all in. Simon should have told me about all this.'

'I can't think why he didn't like the place. It's a terrific house. And I can't wait to explore the gardens.' Verity walked across the room to look at a portrait over the fireplace. 'Is this Simon's father, do you know? It looks modern enough.'

Paula came to stand beside her. 'I suppose it must be, but I've never seen any photographs of him, so I can't know for sure. He died a couple of years before I met Simon. All Simon ever said about him was that he was in his fifties when Simon was born. His mother was in her forties, too, and never got over his birth. She died when Simon was very young, and then a few years later his father married Maggie——' She broke off as the door opened and Maggie came in carrying a silver tea-tray. 'We were just wondering if this was Simon's father,' she said quickly.

'Yes, it is. Although it was painted long before I knew him, of course. He was only about forty then, but he always told me it was a good likeness. Do you think Simon looked much like him?'

After taking a second look at the painting, Paula shook her head. 'No, not really.'

'He must have taken after his mother, then,' Maggie said lightly. She poured out the tea and began to talk easily of other things, the perfect hostess, completely at home in her setting.

As Verity joined in the conversation she wondered if it had been much of a blow to Maggie to find that the house she must look on as her home now belonged to an unborn child. Although she had never owned the house herself, she had been the mistress here for many years; it must be an unsettling time for her now—and for her son. Verity realised that things might be difficult all round, and was doubly glad that she had agreed to come here with Paula.

After tea, Maggie took them upstairs and showed them their rooms, which they were pleased to find were next to each other. Verity looked at her room and thought that it was so large that she could have got the whole ground-floor area of her little house into it. It was high, too, with a beautiful crystal chandelier in the middle of the ceiling, and two wardrobes at least seven feet tall against the far wall. She caught a glimpse of her slim figure in hip-hugging jeans and tight sweater in the full-length mirror on the front of one of the wardrobes, and realised that this was the first piece of furniture in which she'd ever been able to see herself fully. Usually they cut off her legs or the top of her head.

Opening off the bedroom there was a pretty bathroom that smelt of pot-pourri from the large bowl of dried petals on a shelf. Verity decided that she might well be spending a lot of time in there now that she had some leisure on her hands. Which in itself was a strange feeling—usually at home she was always in a mad rush and had little time to spend soaking in the bath. Her cases had been brought up and she methodically unpacked and then went along to Paula's room.

'Hi. Need any help to unpack?'

'I've done a couple of cases, but I think I'll leave the rest till tomorrow.' Paula sat down rather wearily on the bed. 'Perhaps I'll take a nap. There's time before we have to get ready for dinner, isn't there?'

'Of course. It's only five o'clock.'

'How about you?'

Verity glanced towards the window. 'I think I'll go for a walk in the garden before the sun goes down. There's a path that leads to the woods that looks inviting.'

'I'll see you later, then. Wake me when you come back, will you?' Paula lay back on the bed and closed her eyes with a yawn.

'OK. Have a nice sleep.' Verity closed the curtains and hurried back to her own room, where she changed into a pair of flat-heeled boots. Opening the door of the wardrobe, she reached in for a jacket, but the day was still so warm that she settled on a woollen shawl instead, tying it in a loose knot on her shoulder.

There was no one around as she went downstairs. Verity let herself out of the front door and walked briskly past the house and stables, glad to stretch her legs and to get some fresh air. She made a pleasant picture as she strode along, tall and graceful, her shoulder-length chestnut hair lit into a flame as bright as the autumn leaves in the evening sun. Gravel crunched under her feet, but once she had gone past the stables the surface changed to compacted earth with the ruts of tyre marks near the edges.

It was such a lovely day; Verity lifted her head to feel the sun on her face. There was still warmth in it, even so late, and it was so low in the sky and so bright that she had to shade her eyes to see where she was going. The grounds really were beautiful, landscaped to make the most of the terrain, with groups of tall trees that must be as old as the house. A momentary stab of envy filled her as she thought how she would love to live here and how lucky Paula was to have it, but then she immediately felt ashamed as she realised that Paula would give up this and everything else to have Simon alive again.

The sound of water grew louder, although the river didn't seem to be running very fast. To the right the path was bordered by a thick shrubbery, the track converging on the river at the bridge. Grass grew between the tyre ruts and was a little slippery underfoot. Verity moved over to the edge of the road and caught a glimpse of the sun reflecting off water through the bushes on her right. It puzzled her a little, because the water seemed to be at a much lower level, but as she came to the bridge she saw the reason why. Although it was invisible from the garden, the ground fell away steeply behind the shrubbery, dropping down to a quite large lake, thick with weed and lily pads. The water for the lake came from the river and was controlled by a sluice gate just beneath the bridge.

Moving into the shadow thrown by the big chestnut tree, Verity leaned over the low parapet of the bridge and saw that the sluices were partly open, the water gushing down a good ten or twelve feet to make the loud noise she'd heard. The machinery of the sluice was red with rust, the cog-wheels dark and menacing as she looked down on them, the dank smell of wet stone filling her nostrils. A sudden shiver ran through her and she went to turn away, but then a movement caught her eye and she saw a big fish just below the surface of the water. She watched it swim among the stems of the weed, its steely skin like quicksilver in the rippling sunlight, until her attention was caught by a family of ducks down on the other side of the lake. The mother duck was trying to shepherd her five ducklings along, but the last two obviously wanted to play and kept darting behind the lilies, almost as if they were playing hide and seek. Their antics made Verity laugh, and she leaned further over to watch.

The roaring of the water filled her ears and Verity didn't hear the vehicle coming until it was quite close. It was a Land Rover, the sort that farmers used for driving in rough country. It was coming from the direction of the house, the sun reflecting like arrows of light off the windscreen. Verity straightened up in startled alarm and took a hurried step towards the edge of the narrow bridge to get out of the way. She gave a yell of warning and started to raise her arm, her horrified gaze on the Land Rover. It came out of the sunlight into the shade, and for an appalling moment she looked into the face of the man at the wheel, a face that wore a fierce frown of ruthless determination. But then the Land Rover brushed against her and she was sent toppling over the wooden handrail, plunging down towards the dark pit of machinery and stone of the sluice. It all happened so quickly, just a few seconds, and yet Verity's mind had time to realise where she was falling and to fill with terror, knowing that it meant certain injury if not worse.

Perhaps it was terror that gave Verity the strength to grab at the edge of the bridge and cling on, halting her fall. She screamed, her voice stark with fear, as she dangled over the sluice, and somehow managed to swing her other arm upwards so that she was hanging on with both hands. Her shawl slipped from her shoulders and she saw it fall and catch on one of the iron cogs, its ends sucked into the stream of water. Her voice raw with fear, she screamed again, 'Help me! Somebody help me!'

The noise of the rushing water was too loud for her to hear whether or not the Land Rover had stopped, and she couldn't see anything on the bridge, but some instinct cut through her terror and made her look past the bridge over to the right where the road dipped down to the level of the lake and ran along beside it. The Land Rover was there. It had pulled up and the man was getting out. He stood in the shadows, tall and, to her petrified mind, satanic, as he stared across at her slim figure as she hung there. Verity's terrified eyes looked into his and she was filled with the sudden dreadful conviction that he wasn't going to help her, that he was going to stand and watch until she fell.

The scream that broke from her then was one of deathly fear and despair, but suddenly the man seemed to jerk into movement and he came bounding back towards the bridge. Panic seized Verity and her fingers dug into the hard wooden planks as she tried desperately to pull herself back up. She was sure that he meant to break her grip and make her fall. He reached her and bent down, stretched his arms out towards her hands.

'No! No, don't!'

Her petrified cry made him hesitate, and Verity tried to swing away, but then the man's hands had gripped her wrists—and he began to pull her up on to the bridge.

For several minutes she couldn't believe that he was helping her, and she struggled against his hold, yelling and screaming at him to let her go until one of her hands almost slipped from his. He gave a muttered curse, then, and flexed his broad shoulders to suddenly heave her under the parapet and drag her to her feet. The transition from extreme danger to safety was so sudden that Verity was unable to take it in, and she continued to struggle against him, whimpering with terror, until he let her go and stepped back. She stumbled, too overcome by shock to have the strength to stand, and the man quickly stepped forward to catch her again. For a brief second she leant against his chest and felt the arrant masculinity of him, his height and strength, the musky sensuality of his warm skin. She lifted stunned eyes to look at him—and saw again the face of the man who had run her down. With a cry of fear and revulsion, Verity broke loose from his hold and fled back towards the house.

# CHAPTER TWO

VERITY'S terror-stricken run from the bridge to the house was like one of those ghastly nightmares where you were being chased but your legs wouldn't move and no matter how hard you tried you couldn't get away. By the time she reached the front of the house and staggered to the door her breath was coming in hoarse, chest-rending gulps and her legs would hardly carry her. But she opened the door and sent it crashing back against the wall, then made for the stairs, dragging herself up by the banister.

Behind her, she heard a woman's voice call her name, but she ran on up the stairs and almost fell into Paula's room. 'Paula! *Paula!*' Verity dropped to her knees beside the bed and gripped the coverlet, her whole body shaken by terrified sobs.

'Verity? Good heavens, what is it?' Paula sat up and switched on the bedside lamp. 'What's happened?'

'A man. A man, he—he . . .'

Paula stared at her in horror and reached to put her arms round her friend. 'What man? What did he do?'

'Paula, has something happened to Verity? I saw her running in as if the devil were behind her.' Maggie came into the room and crossed it to join them, her voice sharp and a worried frown on her broad brow.

'I don't know. She's in a terrible state. She just said something about a man.' Paula sat on the edge of the

26

bed and stroked Verity's shoulder. 'It's all right, you're safe now. What happened, Verity? Did a man attack you?'

A great shudder ran through her, but Verity managed to shake her head. 'N-no. He—he ran me down.'

'What?' Paula stared at her in horror.

Verity's voice rose hysterically. 'He ran me down! I was standing on the bridge and he knocked me over the edge. I almost fell in the sluice gates. Look! Look at my hands.' She held them out, palm upwards, showing the dirt and splinters embedded in them where she had gripped the wooden planks of the bridge.

'Oh, no! Are you badly hurt? We must call an ambulance, or take you to hospital.'

Paula started to get agitatedly to her feet and Verity belatedly remembered that she was pregnant. Making a brave attempt to control herself, she said unsteadily, 'No. No, I'm all right. Just—just shaken up, that's all.'

'You poor darling.' Paula cradled Verity's head against her shoulder and turned an angry face up to Maggie. 'We must find out who did this at once. Was it one of the gardeners, do you think?'

Her face pale, Maggie shook her head and said in a voice as shocked as Paula's, 'No, the gardener will have gone home by now. I can't think who it could have been. That track only leads from the stables to the old gamekeeper's cottage, where Mr and Mrs Chivers live, and then to the lane leading down to the village. The staff mostly use it as a short cut. I can't think——' She broke off as a sharp knock sounded on the partly open door, and went out into the corridor to see who it was.

'Are you sure you're OK?' Paula said as soon as she'd gone. 'You look terrible.'

'Thanks,' Verity said with a wretched attempt at a wry smile. Pulling herself up, she sat beside Paula on the bed and looked down at her hands. A great quiver of remembered dread ran through her. 'I was so scared. I really thought I'd had it.'

'You were lucky that you were able to climb back up. What did you do, fall on to the bank? You don't seem to be wet at all.'

'No, you don't understand. I caught hold of the bridge as I fell and hung on to it.' Verity gave an exasperated shake of her head. 'You really need to see the place to——'

'But how did you get back up, then?' Paula asked in puzzlement.

Slowly Verity lifted her head and turned to look at Paula, her green eyes wide in her pale face. 'He—the man—he stopped and came back. He pulled me up on to the bridge.'

Paula stared at her. 'But I don't understand. Where is he? Did he bring you back to the house? Why did he——'

She turned impatiently as Maggie came back into the room and closed the door. The older woman stepped slowly across to them, a strange look on her face as she glanced at Verity. 'That was my son, Sebastian. It seems that he was the one who knocked you off the bridge. It was purely an accident, of course,' Maggie added quickly, 'but he's naturally very worried about you. He came here at once to find out how you were. He said that you seemed all right when he rescued you, but he can't understand why you ran away from him and wouldn't let him help you any further.'

Both Verity's and Paula's eyes widened. 'Your son?' Paula exclaimed. 'But I thought you said he wasn't coming home until tonight.'

'He managed to get back earlier than he'd expected,' Maggie explained. 'But then he remembered some business he had with Chivers, and he went to drive over there, and that's when he ran into—that is, knocked against . . . Oh, dear, I really think I ought to let him explain for himself. He's waiting outside. May he come in? I know he's very anxious to see for himself that you're all right, Verity.' As she spoke Maggie moved towards the door and stretched out her hand to the knob.

Getting agitatedly to her feet, Verity said sharply, 'No!' And then, trying hard to control herself, 'No, please. I—I really don't want to see him. I——' She broke off, unable to say what she really felt and too distraught to find a tactful way of putting it.

Maggie frowned and said stiffly, 'Sebastian assures me that the—the incident was quite accidental. He had the sun in his eyes and just didn't see you. But I'm sure that he can explain much better than I can, if you'll just talk to him.'

'No, not—not now, please. I—my hands . . .'

She lifted them again, almost pleadingly, and Paula came to her aid by saying quickly, 'I really think it would be better if Verity had a little time to recover first, don't you? After all, she's had a nasty shock. And I must clean up her hands. Do you have a first-aid kit?'

'Why, yes, of course. I—I'll fetch it.' But Maggie looked uncertainly at Verity. 'But what shall I tell Sebastian?'

'Oh, just that we'll see him at dinner,' Paula replied in her sweetest voice, and gave Maggie a disarming smile.

When Paula smiled like that there were few people who could resist her, and, somewhat mollified, Maggie went away to find the first-aid box. Verity was in Paula's bathroom when she returned with it and didn't see her; she was sitting on a chair with her eyes closed and fighting hard to stop herself shaking.

'Here, let me see.' Paula gently took hold of one of her hands and began to bathe it. 'Now tell me exactly what happened,' she commanded.

Slowly, her voice often breaking, Verity did so.

Paula heard her out, then said, 'And you're convinced that he—Sebastian—deliberately ran you down?'

'Yes. I know it sounds crazy,' Verity began, her voice rising, 'but I'm sure he did.'

'All right, I believe you,' Paula said soothingly. 'But he says that the sun was in his eyes and he didn't see you.' She took both of Verity's hands in hers. 'Maybe you ought to hear what he has to say before you accuse him of anything.'

'You don't believe me,' Verity said flatly and tried to draw away.

But Paula hung on. 'I believe that you're convinced in your own mind that it was deliberate,' she assured Verity. 'But why on earth should he *do* a thing like that? It just doesn't make sense.'

Verity looked at her unhappily. 'Do you think I don't know that? He must be some kind of maniac!'

'Oh, Verity, come on. He's Simon's stepbrother, Maggie's son, not some poor madman who's escaped from an asylum. Why on earth would he run you down?'

'I don't know!' Verity said sharply and got to her feet. 'I only know that he did.' She swung round on her friend. 'You're convinced that I'm wrong, aren't you? But, Paula, you didn't see his face—*and I did*. It was full of anger and determination and—and hate almost. For that split second before he hit me I saw all that, and I'm sure he meant to hit me!'

It took a great deal of persuasion from Paula and a lot of courage on Verity's part for her to go down to dinner an hour or so later. But Paula fussed around her, making her put on a deep green two-piece outfit that brought out the colour of her eyes, and drawing her hair back from her face, even making Verity spray on some of her best perfume. 'There,' Paula remarked as she drew her friend over to the full-length mirror. 'If you must face Sebastian, you can at least do it looking your best. Looking good is a girl's best armour, you know.'

Verity nodded, but somehow didn't feel that the girl reflected in the mirror was herself; the face was too pale despite the make-up, and there was still a frightened, almost hunted look in the eyes. A quiver ran through her and she turned to Paula with an appealing look. 'Paula, I really can't face him.'

'Yes, you can,' the other girl replied firmly. 'Look, you've got to see Sebastian some time. You can't live in the same house and keep avoiding him. It's ridiculous! So you might as well get it over with now. Come on; I'm usually the coward, not you. You're always the one who's so strong and brave.'

'Well, I don't feel in the least brave now,' Verity answered feelingly. But she allowed Paula to take her arm and lead her downstairs.

They were waiting for them in the drawing-room, Maggie Layton and her son. Maggie was sitting on a settee, rather nervously flicking through a magazine, but Sebastian was standing by the fireplace, a foot on the fender and an elbow propped on the high mantelshelf. Verity's eyes went immediately to him, and then instantly looked away, but she was aware of height and strength, of searching grey eyes under a broad brow, and a tension that was belied by his casual stance.

Maggie got to her feet and came forward. 'Let me introduce you,' she said quickly. 'Sebastian, this is your sister-in-law, Paula, and her friend Verity Mitchell. My son, Sebastian Kent.'

Paula went forward first and, after a moment's hesitation, gave an uncertain smile and shook the hand that Sebastian held out to her. They didn't speak, and both turned almost immediately to where Verity stood nervously near the door, looking poised to run away at any sudden move. It seemed so strange to be introduced formally like that to a man who had nearly killed her.

Sebastian took a couple of steps towards her, and then stopped as he saw her recoil in alarm. A frown that Verity remembered vividly creased his brow, and the grey eyes became cold and withdrawn as he said shortly, 'Miss Mitchell, I am most dreadfully sorry for what happened. Mother tells me that you weren't hurt, but it must have been a terrible shock for you.' He paused for a moment, but when she didn't speak went on, 'I can only repeat my apology. I'm afraid the sun was in my eyes and you were in the shadow. I was only aware of you at the very last second. In fact, at first I thought I must have been mistaken. It was only when I saw you hanging from the bridge that I realised what must have happened——' He stopped rather abruptly, his mouth thinning, as if he didn't enjoy the role of an apologist and already felt that he had said more than enough.

For the life of her Verity couldn't find anything to say to him. She could only stand, feeling angry and frustrated, and look into his cold eyes with fascinated fear. She was safe now, she knew that, but there was nothing in the least reassuring in Sebastian's manner— even his apology had been uttered in an abrupt, aloof tone.

'I expect you'd like a drink.'

'Verity, come and sit down.'

Both Maggie and Paula broke into the heavy silence, Paula taking Verity's arm and leading her to a settee. She sank on to it and took the drink that Maggie held out to her. It was gin and it tasted good, but her hand trembled as she held the glass. She glanced up and found that Sebastian was watching her, a brooding expression on his face. She took another hasty gulp of the gin and was grateful when Paula, ever tactful, started asking questions about the house, drawing both Sebastian and Maggie into the conversation and so giving Verity a chance to recover.

But she still hadn't said a word when they all went into dinner. Normally she would have been bug-eyed at the beauty of the panelled room with its paintings and Chinese carpet, the delicate lace tablecloth and the exquisite china, but tonight she hardly bothered to look around her before she sat down in her place.

Maggie served the first course from a heated trolley. It was soup and it smelt good, but Verity found that she couldn't eat. The others were still talking about the house, but she was unaware of what they were saying. All she heard was Sebastian's deep voice speaking in a detached tone as if there was absolutely nothing the matter, as if he hadn't just tried to run her down and injure her. It was an attractive voice, with that rich masculine timbre that some actors were fortunate enough to have, the sort of voice that could woo you with words.

Suddenly fed up with pretending that everything was normal, Verity lifted her head and glared at him antagonistically. It disconcerted him. For a second Sebastian hesitated as he caught her glance, but it was only for a moment, and then he went on with what he was saying as smoothly as ever. But when he'd finished he turned to her and said, 'I see your hands have dressings on them. Did that happen when you fell from the bridge?'

In view of the look she'd thrown him, the question was almost a challenge. It also implied that it was her own fault. Verity's chin came up and she said coldly, 'You mean when you knocked me over? Yes, it did.'

Paula gave her a shocked look and said hastily, 'But they really aren't too bad. It was mostly splinters that had gone deep. In a way I suppose she was lucky...' Her voice trailed off as she encountered a fiery glance from Verity and there was an embarrassed silence.

Into it Sebastian said in a decisive tone, 'Verity is obviously still very upset, which is completely natural. She blames me for the accident and she is right to do so.' He turned to look at her directly. 'But I think it would be better for everyone if we tried to put it out of our minds for——'

He would have continued, but Verity said angrily, 'You mean just forget it ever happened?'

'I wasn't going to say forever. I merely meant for the present, at least until after dinner. I——'

Bright spots of colour rose in her pale cheeks as Verity said sarcastically, 'Oh, I agree that would be far more civilised, far more *convenient*—especially for you! But right now I don't feel very conciliatory.' She threw her napkin on to the table and began to stand up. 'I'm sorry, Paula, I don't feel like eating anything.'

But Paula gave her an agonised look and grabbed her wrist. 'You made me a promise. *Remember?*' she hissed in a fierce undertone.

Verity looked at her mutinously for a moment, but then she realised how embarrassing and difficult it would be for Paula if she just abandoned her to her in-laws on her first evening at Layton House. Slowly, reluctantly, Verity sat down again; Paula had been nervous enough before, now that this had happened it would be even less fair to walk out on her, much as she hated the idea of having to be even remotely polite to Sebastian. But she was rewarded with a look of deep relief from Paula, who turned and began to talk to Maggie again.

Picking up her bread roll from the side plate, Verity broke it into pieces, her head lowered. She felt cold, although the house was very warm. But the coldness was entirely anger at Sebastian's high-handedness. OK, so he had apologised, but there had been no real concern in his voice. Verity thought he would probably have used the same tone for something utterly trivial, like treading on her toe. She glanced at him under her lashes and saw with annoyance that he seemed quite calm. As if he felt her eyes on him, Sebastian looked up, his lips thinning as he saw that she wasn't making any attempt to eat.

'I understand that you had trouble with your car on the way here?' he remarked.

The question was directed at Verity, but both Maggie and Paula paused in what they were saying while they listened for her answer, or perhaps to hear if she would answer at all. Verity knew that to make any kind of a reply to such a mundane remark would be an acceptance, an admission that she might be wrong and that it could have been an accident after all. She would have liked to just ignore Sebastian, or better still to tell him to go to hell, but she was fully aware of Paula's inner anxiety, of the tension in her friend's taut body beside her, and she knew that for her sake she must make some show of reconciliation. So she said heavily, 'Yes, we had trouble with the petrol pump and had to have a new one fitted.'

Paula gave an almost audible sigh of relief and resumed her conversation with Maggie, her voice lighter now. Verity had kept her eyes averted from Sebastian as she spoke, but she could almost feel his triumph. 'Is it running all right now?' he asked in a maddeningly conversational tone. 'I could always get our local mechanic to check it over for you, if you're at all worried.'

'That won't be necessary,' Verity said crisply. 'If I want it looked at I can take it to a garage myself.'

Sebastian nodded, ignoring the acidity of her tone. He shot her a glance, his grey eyes assessing the anger that still lingered in her flushed cheeks. 'Perhaps you'd care for another roll,' he said sardonically, and held the basket out to her.

She was puzzled for a second, but then looked down at her plate and saw that her roll was now nothing but a pile of crumbs. Quickly she dropped the piece she was still holding, and put her hands in her lap, annoyed with herself for betraying weakness. Lifting her head, she shot Sebastian an angry glare, but was surprised to see a small smile on his lips and a look almost of understanding in his eyes. Her heart gave a little jump, taken aback by this sudden change. It was as if an eagle had suddenly turned into a dove, a transformation that was as unexpected as it was unbelievable. Verity frowned, and thought that she would as soon trust a snake.

The meal seemed to drag, although in fact was over very quickly, all four of them anxious to leave the confines of the table and the need to make small talk. Maggie suggested they have coffee in the drawing-room, but she had promised to show Paula the nursery that Simon had used as a child and Paula eagerly asked to go and see it at once.

'Of course. It's this way.' And Maggie turned to go up the stairs.

Verity was about to follow the other two women, but Sebastian put a restraining hand on her arm. 'Please; I'd like to talk to you.'

His touch confused her. She tried to shake him off, but found his grip unexpectedly firm. She threw a hunted glance up to the landing where Paula and Maggie were just turning down the corridor, apparently oblivious of the fact that she wasn't with them. 'There's really nothing you can say to me that will——'

'But I think there is,' Sebastian cut in smoothly and, still holding her arm, led her into the drawing-room and shut the door. He let her go then, but leant back against the door, watching her.

She felt trapped, with him leaning against the door like that, his broad shoulders a physical bar. 'Well, what is it you want to say to me?' she snapped.

'I'd just like to know why you're so convinced that what happened this afternoon wasn't an accident,' Sebastian said bluntly. 'I can't even understand how you can think anything else.'

This direct attack threw Verity for a moment, but her chin came up and she said, 'I'm sure that you saw me, that you——'

Sebastian gave an impatient shake of his head. 'I've already explained that the sun was in my eyes. If you remember, it was very low in the sky at that time.'

'Maybe it was,' she admitted, 'but you could have stopped or at least swerved out of the way.'

An exasperated frown creased his brow. 'But I didn't see you, I tell you.'

'You must have done. I saw you—perfectly clearly. And if I could see you, then you must have been able to see me.'

He stared at her, his grey eyes intense. 'Do you realise what you're saying?' he demanded harshly. 'You're accusing me of deliberately running you down. Perhaps even of trying to kill you.'

Verity took a trembling breath. 'Yes, I know.'

His eyes widened incredulously. 'And just why on earth should I want to do that? I'm not in the habit of running down complete strangers, you know,' he added sarcastically.

'No, I don't know,' Verity answered tartly. 'I only have your word for it.'

'Well, really! This is the outside of enough.' Sebastian made an angry gesture with his arm and took a few strides round the room before coming to a menacing stop in front of her. 'I just can't understand why you're so convinced,' he said in mounting anger. 'Why you won't even begin to listen to me.' He made a visible effort to control his temper and said, 'Look, will you at least admit that it was possible for me not to have seen you when I was driving towards you with the sun shining into the windscreen and when you were standing in a block of shade?'

Slowly Verity nodded. 'Yes, I suppose that's possible.'

'Well, that's something anyway. Now, you say that you saw me clearly. When was that?'

'You know when.' Sebastian gave her an angry glare and she said, 'Oh, very well. It was in the few seconds when you came out of the sun into the shadow of the tree. I saw your face clearly then...' Her features tightened as she remembered that look of fury in his face and she raised wide, accusing eyes to meet his. 'I don't think I'll ever forget that moment.'

He stared at her, shocked by the sudden emotion in her eyes and voice. 'Why not?' He put a hand on her arm, his face earnest. 'Verity, please tell me why you're so certain that I wilfully tried to do such a terrible thing to you.'

She gazed into his face, aware only now of how lean and clear-cut his features were, and suddenly it seemed impossible for him to have done it deliberately. He was so self-controlled, so cool, so *sane*. Turning her head away, she said unsteadily, 'In that moment when I saw your face, you—you looked so fierce, as if you were furiously angry. And you were looking straight at me! What else was I to think? I——' She broke off, biting her lip, aware that she was becoming defensive.

Letting go of her arm, Sebastian straightened up, squaring his shoulders. There was a frown in his eyes and he didn't speak at once, as if he was making up his mind about something. Finally he said, 'Verity, I realise that I have no right to ask any favours of you when you've already suffered so much at my hands, but——'

'But you're going to ask it anyway,' she broke in.

He gave a twisted, rueful smile. 'Yes, I am. Because it's very important to me that we get this thing sorted out.' His eyes held hers. 'I don't want you to go on having the wrong idea about me, you see.'

His voice was deep, insinuating, and she was very aware of his sheer masculine attraction. 'What—what favour do you want?' she asked a little unsteadily.

'I want you to come with me tomorrow, at the same time as the accident happened, to the same place, and see for yourself how difficult it was for me to see you. Hopefully the weather tomorrow will be much the same as today. Will you do that for me, Verity?' he asked urgently.

She hesitated, realising that she had already relented a good deal. 'You want me to admit that I might have been mistaken?'

'I want you to see for yourself that it's possible,' he corrected her. 'Will you come?'

'Yes, all right. But...' she lifted her head to look directly into his eyes '...you haven't yet explained why you were so angry with me.'

At that he gave a decisive shake of his head. 'Not with you, no. How could I possibly be when I didn't even know you? But—well, I admit that I was extremely angry at the time. It was—something to do with the estate, nothing more. But I'm terribly afraid that my mind was preoccupied with that, and I wasn't concentrating as well as I might on my driving. Add that to the sun and not expecting anyone to be on the bridge, and I'm afraid it all adds up to what could have been a terrible tragedy, for which I can only apologise yet again.' There was real emotion in his voice this time, as if he was picturing it all over again, as he added, 'I would never have been able to live with myself if——'

He turned away rather abruptly, took a few paces round the room, his hands thrust into his pockets. 'Thank you for saying that you'll come tomorrow,' he said at length. 'I appreciate it, after all you've been through.'

Verity wasn't quite sure what to say to that, but the sound of the door opening made them both turn as Paula and Maggie came into the room, the two women giving them quick, searching looks as they entered.

'Good heavens, haven't you brought the coffee in yet?' Maggie remarked, and went out to the kitchen to fetch it.

'What was the nursery like?' Verity asked, turning to Paula in some relief.

'Lovely! Terribly old-fashioned, of course, but there are some gorgeous toys up there. A huge rocking-horse, and a train set. Lots of things that Simon used to play with.'

Paula spoke brightly enough, but Verity knew her friend very well and recognised from the shadowed look in her eyes and the break in her tone that she was missing Simon. Quickly Verity went over and linked her arm through Paula's. 'Come and sit down and tell me all about it. Will you redecorate the room, do you think? What colour will you do it? I saw some delightful nursery wallpaper in a store in London recently.'

The questions soon diverted Paula and her face brightened. She loved designing and decorating; before her marriage she had worked for a large firm of interior designers in London, and it was when the firm had sent her to Bahrain to redesign the home of one of their rich Arab clients that she had met Simon.

They were still discussing the subject when Maggie returned with the coffee-tray. 'Would you mind if I had the nursery redecorated?' Paula said rather hesitantly as she took the cup that Sebastian offered her. 'Perhaps you would rather it was left as it is.'

'It's sweet of you to ask,' Maggie answered. 'But this is your house now, Paula. You can do as you please with it. Or at least, it's your child's—Simon's child's.'

'But it's been your home for so long,' Paula began. 'I'm sure that you must rese——' She broke off, her cheeks colouring in embarrassment. 'That is, I——'

'It was bound to happen sooner or later,' Sebastian said brusquely. 'Presumably Simon would have brought you back here eventually. As far as my mother and I are concerned, we've just been caretakers here ever since my stepfather—Simon's father—died.'

He spoke so harshly that Verity looked at him searchingly, wondering if he resented the invidious position that Simon had left him in. It couldn't have been easy for him to have a younger stepbrother who had inherited everything while he had nothing. Especially when Simon had treated his home and his inheritance with such disregard, as if it was of little or no importance to him.

As if he heard the harshness in his own voice, Sebastian modulated his tone as he said to Paula, 'Perhaps you could spare some time tomorrow morning to discuss the estate and your plans with me? And you'll want to go through the books, of course. They're dealt with on a day-to-day basis by a local firm of accountants, but I'll get them to send the books over so that you——'

'Oh, no, please!' Paula broke in, 'I'm sure that's not necessary. Simon always said that you ran the estate far more efficiently than he ever could. He had no head for anything at all agricultural.'

'Nevertheless, I must insist that we have a talk as soon as possible,' Sebastian persisted. 'Would ten-thirty tomorrow be convenient?'

It was more of a command than a request. Paula agreed, but gave Verity a look of helpless appeal—a look that was put into words when the two girls went up to bed an hour or so later. 'Come into my room for a while,' Paula said urgently. And when the door was safely shut, 'Lord, what a day! I'm glad it's over.' Sitting on the bed, she kicked off her shoes. 'Well, at least we can't say that it's boring in the country. Though I'm not particularly looking forward to tomorrow, either.'

'Why not? You're not worrying about the meeting with Sebastian, are you?'

'Yes, I am,' Paula said feelingly. 'What if he wants me to take over the running of the estate? I know even less about that sort of thing than Simon did.'

'I'm sure he doesn't expect that,' Verity said reassuringly. 'He probably just wants you to give him the go-ahead to carry on as before. Anybody would in his position.'

'Do you think I ought to offer to pay him or something?' Paula asked worriedly. 'I don't even know if Simon paid him a salary.'

'Well, I expect he'll tell you that tomorrow. Sebastian doesn't strike me as being the type who's afraid to come out and say what's on his mind,' Verity said wryly.

Paula gave her a look brim full of curiosity. 'What happened between you and Sebastian while Maggie and I were upstairs? I didn't know whether to hurry down and rescue you or leave you to sort it out between you. I was half afraid you might have a fight.'

'We came close,' Verity admitted. 'But I suppose the accident must have shaken me up more than I realised, because I——'

'Accident? Are you saying that you believe Sebastian now?'

Verity frowned broodingly. 'Let's say I'm beginning to have second thoughts now that I've got over the shock of it a bit more. It just seems so impossible for it to have been anything else. And Sebastian—well, how could anyone conceivably think of him as some kind of maniac? When you talk to him—well, he just doesn't fit the part.'

Leaning back against the bedhead, Paula said, 'What did you think of him?'

'Physically, you mean?'

'Mmm, and as a person.'

'Well, physically he's OK, I suppose, and——'

'Oh, come off it, Verity; he's terrifically attractive! Tall, dark, and handsome in a hard kind of way; what more could you want? And don't tell me you haven't noticed.'

'I was too busy wondering why the hell he wanted to kill me to worry about what he looked like,' Verity answered shortly. But then she saw Paula raise her eyebrows disbelievingly, and said, 'Oh, OK, maybe he is good-looking, but, like you said, there's something about him, something hard and cold under the surface that gives me the shivers.'

'He is rather intimidating at times,' Paula admitted. 'But he can be very charming, too.'

'*All* men can be charming when they want to be,' Verity pointed out with certainty.

'That's true.'

Both girls fell silent for a moment, each busy with her own thoughts, then Paula yawned. 'Oh, I'm tired. It's been a long day.'

'I'll leave you to get some sleep, then,' Verity said, standing up at once. 'Don't forget I'm right next door if you need me.'

'Thanks.' Paula caught Verity's arm as she went to leave. 'I'm so glad that you're all right. Oh, Verity, I couldn't bear it if something terrible happened to you, too.'

'It won't.' Verity sat down again and put a comforting arm round Paula's shoulders. 'Surely today must have proved to you that I have a charmed life?'

'And it *was* an accident, wasn't it?' Paula asked in sudden anxiety.

Realising that to reassure Paula was all-important, Verity said with a confidence that she was beginning to feel might be real, 'Of course it was. I was a fool to even think for a moment that Sebastian did it deliberately. Put it down to shock and my vivid imagination.'

'And you'll stay here with me? You won't let it put you off?'

'Of course not. OK, so maybe I got off to a bad start with Sebastian, but Maggie has been very kind and welcoming. You'll be happy here, you'll see. Tomorrow we'll explore the house and the garden, and then you can decide how you want the nursery and we'll decorate it together; I've become quite good at painting and wallpapering since I bought my house.'

She stayed for a while longer, talking Paula into a more secure frame of mind, and only left when the other girl began to sag with tiredness and would soon fall asleep and forget her worries. 'Goodnight. See you tomorrow.'

Paula yawned again. 'Oh, dear, I have that meeting with Sebastian tomorrow,' she remembered.

'Don't worry about it; you needn't be afraid of Sebastian.'

Verity went to her own room and got ready for bed. She, too, felt very tired, and her shoulders ached where she had hung from the bridge. She lifted her hands to rub them and felt a cold shiver run through her. Resolutely she tried to put the memories out of her mind, and got into bed, putting out the light and lying in the darkness waiting for sleep to come. But every time she closed her eyes she saw again Sebastian's face, full of anger, and hastily opened them. She had confidently told Paula not to worry about her meeting with Sebastian tomorrow, that she needn't be afraid of him, but she had also promised to meet Sebastian tomorrow—and she very much wished that she could believe her own words, because she felt more than a little apprehensive and worried about what that meeting might bring.

# CHAPTER THREE

STRANGELY, Verity woke quite early the next morning and didn't feel at all tired, although it had been late before she had finally got to sleep. Sunlight filtered through a gap in the curtains and she got quickly out of bed to pull them aside. A thin carpet of mist lay over the dew-soaked lawns surrounding the house, but the birds were already singing their hearts out, making the most of the sun. Opening the window, Verity leaned her elbows on the sill and looked out, fleetingly glad that her room wasn't at the front of the house and so didn't overlook the river and the bridge.

It was going to be a beautiful day. Ordinarily she would have been rushing to queue for a bus and then push her way on to a crowded underground train to get to work. But not today. Today she was free, at least until this afternoon when she had promised to meet Sebastian. Pushing that thought out of her mind, Verity showered and dressed, putting on a full skirt and baggy sweater, and then ran downstairs. There was no one in the dining-room or drawing-room, but she could hear sounds coming from a room down the hallway and pushed open the door to find herself in a big farmhouse-style kitchen. A woman was working at an Aga oven built against the far wall, its warmth giving a pleasing feeling of welcome to the room. The woman turned round—and the feeling of welcome vanished. She gave Verity a look of open hostility, the small eyes in her rather fat face going over her in apparent dislike.

Verity stopped on the threshold, taken aback by such unexpected animosity. 'G-good morning,' she stammered, completely thrown.

The woman's glare only increased. 'I suppose you'll be Mrs Layton,' she said in a disparaging tone.

'Why, no. I'm Verity Mitchell, Paula—Mrs Layton's friend.'

'Oh, the other one.' The woman sniffed, but some of the antagonism left her face.

'Er—yes.' Verity gave her a puzzled frown and dredged her memory to come up with a name. 'And I suppose you're Mrs Chivers?'

'Who told you about me?' the woman immediately demanded belligerently.

'I believe the other Mrs Layton, Maggie, mentioned your name yesterday,' Verity answered coolly. 'And doesn't that bacon smell as if it's burning?'

The woman quickly turned back to the stove and removed a frying pan from the hotplate. 'I suppose you'll be wanting your breakfast. If you wait in the morning-room, I'll bring it in to you.'

'Thanks, but I only want some juice. And I'll take some up for Mrs Paula Layton.' It was going to be awkward with two Mrs Laytons in the house, Verity realised. Ordinarily she would just have said Paula, but Mrs Chivers' attitude and her own inexperience in dealing with domestic staff made her speak more formally than she would ordinarily have done.

The cupboards round the room were glass-fronted, so Verity was able to find and take down two glasses, which she filled with orange juice from a carton in the fridge. She was aware of Mrs Chivers' disapproving eyes watching her as she did so, but the housekeeper didn't say anything more, turning away to put the bacon she'd cooked into a sandwich for herself, which she began to eat.

'I'll let you know if Mrs Layton wants anything more for breakfast,' Verity said as she backed out of the door carrying a tray with the two glasses.

Mrs Chivers had sat down at the kitchen table and just gave her a dour look before turning away to read a newspaper.

What a horrible woman! Verity wondered why on earth Maggie put up with her, but perhaps it was difficult to get staff to work in a big country house like this, and perhaps Mrs Chivers resented having two extra people to cope with, not to mention the baby when it came along. Resentment—there was the word again, an emotion which seemed to be in people's minds even if not spoken, although Verity had to admit that neither Maggie nor Sebastian had shown it. The house, though, looked well cared for, so presumably Mrs Chivers was a hard worker. Anyway, it was none of Verity's business; all she could do was to offer to help so that she and Paula wouldn't be too much of a burden.

It was too nice to stay indoors. A table and some chairs in heavy, white-painted wrought-ironwork had been set out on the patio outside the drawing-room; Verity sat down there to drink her juice, enjoying the freshness of the morning. The patio was a sun-trap, facing south and sheltered from any breeze by the two projecting wings of the house. The rich scent of warm earth and damp grass filled the air, unfamiliar to Verity's town-bred senses, yet reaching some primitive part of her nature that instantly recognised the

aromas and found them good, even sensuous. Leaning
her head back, she closed her eyes, drinking in the
scents, her hair falling back from her head and glistening with the sheen of new chestnuts in the sun.

Lost in her reverie, Verity didn't hear someone else
come out on to the patio until Sebastian's voice said
'Good morning' close behind her. She jerked her head
forward and swung round in startled alarm, her arms
coming up in a protective movement as she half rose
from her seat, banging her hip against the table as
she did so.

'It's all right,' Sebastian said sardonically at her
reaction, 'I'm not going to attack you.'

Slowly she subsided into her chair, rubbing her hip.
'You made me jump. I was miles away and I hadn't
heard you.'

He gave her a brooding look. 'I suppose you have
the right to be jumpy after yesterday.'

Verity gave a short laugh. 'Well, I'm not usually
the nervous type.'

'No.' Sebastian pulled out a chair and sat down
beside her, his eyes going over her as if assessing her
all over again in the light of day. 'No, I don't think
you are.' He gave a rather rueful grin. 'We haven't
exactly met in the most fortuitous of circumstances,
have we? But maybe we can put that right today. *I*
certainly hope so.'

There was just enough emphasis on the pronoun to
make Verity give him a quick, surprised glance. She
was attractive enough to have heard that tone in a
man's voice many times before, although she hadn't
expected to hear it now. But there was nothing in
Sebastian's face to suggest that he fancied her, no
raised eyebrows or knowing smile, and she thought

she must have been mistaken, that he just wanted her to admit that she'd been wrong yesterday and clear him of any blame. Yes, that must be it, but the idea that he might be interested in her had made Verity become more interested in him. She wondered if he had a girlfriend and why he had never married. Or perhaps he had been married and it hadn't worked out. She really knew hardly anything about him, and didn't think that Paula knew much more.

His mouth thinned. 'I see you're reserving judgement.'

'Perhaps. I was just thinking that I know very little about you,' Verity admitted honestly.

'Or I you.' Sebastian grinned suddenly, and the smile transfigured his face. 'For instance, I don't know why you need two glasses of orange juice.'

'What? Oh, the other one is for Paula. But I shouldn't think she'll be awake yet.' She glanced at her watch. 'I'll take it up to her shortly.'

Reaching out, Sebastian turned her wrist so that he, too, could see her watch. 'Almost eight. I'd better make a move; I have some business to attend to before I have that chat with Paula.' He stood up and raised his hand in a casual gesture of farewell. 'See you about five this evening.'

He strode away from her, not back into the house, but through the garden and round towards the garages, a tall, broad-shouldered figure in a well-cut country tweed jacket. Verity watched him go, wondering why he had chosen to look at her watch when he had an expensive gold one on his own wrist, and also realising that he had very cleverly avoided telling her anything at all about himself. He was, she decided, a very enigmatic man, perhaps a very private one, who would give nothing of himself away unless he wanted to.

Verity sat on in the sun, pondering Sebastian as she finished her juice. It was going to feel odd living in the same house as him—and with Maggie, of course. Strangers thrown together by an act of fate. Maybe it might not be such a good idea to get to know him better, perhaps it would be wiser to keep a distance between them, be polite but cool. After all, she was here as Paula's friend and morale booster, and that way, if there were any future disagreements about the running of the house or the estate, she wouldn't have any feelings of divided loyalty.

Paula was still asleep when Verity went up some twenty minutes later. She woke when Verity opened the curtains, and the two chatted until Paula took her bath. She seemed better this morning, and, apart from being a little nervous about her interview with Sebastian, was happy enough. Sometimes Paula still felt a little queasy in the mornings, so she said very definitely that she didn't want a cooked breakfast, and the two girls went to the nursery and spent a contented hour working out what work needed doing on the room until it was time for Paula's talk with Sebastian.

'Wish me luck,' Paula said feelingly. 'I think I may need it.'

'Nonsense, you'll be fine. And Sebastian seems to be in quite a good mood this morning.'

'You've seen him?'

'Yes. He's obviously another person who likes to be up and about early.'

Paula pulled a face at her; it was an old joke between them that Paula hated getting up in the mornings.

Verity went with her as far as Sebastian's study and made a fingers-crossed sign as Paula tapped and went in. Left with nothing to do, Verity went in search of Maggie and found her in the kitchen, but there was no sign of Mrs Chivers, which was something of a relief.

'Hello,' Verity smiled. 'I wondered if I could help in any way.'

'That's kind of you. Here, you can peel some apples. I'm making a whole batch of apple pies so that I can freeze them.'

Verity pulled a kitchen stool up to the table, glad that she wasn't being treated as a guest and shooed out of the way. 'You don't do all the cooking, do you?' she asked as she set to work.

'I cook lunch for myself and any guests, and Sebastian when he's home, but Mrs Chivers comes in early to do Sebastian's breakfast, and then again in the afternoon to prepare dinner, which she leaves ready for me to finish off and serve.'

'Oh, yes, I met Mrs Chivers this morning.'

There must have been some reserve in Verity's voice because Maggie looked at her keenly and then gave a small sigh. 'Oh, dear, I hope she wasn't rude to you. You'll have to forgive her, I'm afraid; she's been unwell and there have been some personal problems. They've made her rather difficult and short-tempered. We're used to her, of course.'

'She's been here a long time, has she?'

'Oh, ages. She and her husband came to work here before I married Simon's father.'

So that explained Mrs Chivers' surly attitude, and perhaps, too, the woman felt that Paula was a usurper and feared for her job, especially as her home evidently went with the job. Verity sighed inwardly, thinking how difficult it all was for Paula. Which was a great shame, because the last thing Paula wanted at the moment was more anxiety on top of Simon's death. And *she* hadn't helped at all yesterday when she'd wildly accused Sebastian of running her down, Verity realised with some shame. But at least she could put that right by reassuring Paula that she'd been mistaken and never referring to it again, she decided. *If* she'd been mistaken. For a few seconds doubt filled her mind again, but she was already more than half convinced that she had been completely wrong about Sebastian. He just wasn't the type to——

'Do you like cooking?'

Maggie's question broke into her thoughts and Verity smiled and said, 'Yes, I do rather, although I live by myself, so there doesn't seem to be much point in cooking when it's so much easier to buy ready-made meals.'

'You live in London, don't you?'

'Yes.' Verity let herself be drawn into talking about her home, her work as a computer programmer, and her friendship with Paula. After all, Maggie must be as curious about them as they were about the people at Layton House.

'And you gave up your job to come here with Paula!' Maggie exclaimed in surprise. 'Was that really necessary?'

'Paula said she needed me,' Verity answered simply. 'But I'm sure she'll soon settle down and be OK on her own,' she added quickly, in case Maggie took the remark personally.

The older woman smiled. 'Pregnant women need the support of someone close. There,' she stood up and went to get a saucepan. 'I think we can start cooking these now.'

They worked together until Paula came into the kitchen to find them with the message that Sebastian wouldn't be in to lunch. Verity gave her a quick, interrogative look and saw that Paula had a rather dazed expression on her face, but she had to wait until they'd eaten a simple salad lunch with Maggie before she could ask what had happened in the interview with Sebastian.

On the pretext of getting some fresh air, they went out into the garden and Verity said, 'Well? Come on, tell me all about it. You looked quite stunned earlier.'

'I was stunned. I still am. Verity, I had absolutely no idea how much Simon was worth. I thought there was just the business and an insurance policy he took out. But Sebastian said——' She stopped and turned to Verity. 'I'm rich! Really rich. Or at least the baby is, but as its legal guardian I have the power to do what I like with the money. Or I will have when it's born, not now.' She shook her head in some bewilderment. 'I just can't believe it.'

Verity laughed. 'So it seems. Look, there's a seat over there, come and tell me all about it.'

They sat down and Paula began to talk excitedly, telling Verity that the estate had appreciated in value over the last years and drew in a large annual income from rented-out houses and business premises in the surrounding villages and nearby town. There was also a large portfolio of shares that Simon's father had left in trust to Simon and his heirs.

'And what about Sebastian?' Verity asked curiously.

'Oh, everything goes to him if anything happens to the baby,' Paula answered. 'He was careful to explain that it was all entailed until the child comes of age and wouldn't automatically be mine.' But she didn't sound too unhappy about it.

'That wasn't what I meant; I just wondered what Sebastian was like during the interview. But, Paula, are you saying that if anything should happen to the baby before he's eighteen then you'll be left with nothing?'

'Oh, no, I'll still have the money from the business and the insurance policy; that's mine no matter what.'

Verity sat back with a frown. 'I think you ought to consult a solicitor about all this.'

'Yes, that's what Sebastian suggested. In fact, I'm going to see the family solicitor in a couple of days; he made the appointment for me this morning.' Paula turned to look at her. 'Sebastian went into everything very carefully, and showed me all the account books. Not that I really understood them. But he was very patient.'

'Did he ask you what your plans were, or say what he and Maggie wanted to do?'

'He said that I was to take as much time as I wanted and to let him know whenever I decide to make any changes. He said that he and Maggie would quite understand, so I suppose that means that if I want them to go, then they'll go,' Paula said, the dazed note still in her voice.

'He said that? And he was OK about it, not cold or nasty or anything.'

'No, he was marvellous. Anyone would think that they would be quite glad to move out. Oh, but he did say that until the baby is born I can't legally take over the estate as his guardian.'

'So you can't really make any changes—or have them leave—until then?'

'No. But I don't really want to, anyway.' Paula reached out to take Verity's hand. 'Maybe it will be rather nice to have a family again, even if it is a second-hand one. We haven't been very lucky as far as families go, have we?'

'No.' Verity looked down at their joined hands for a moment, but then straightened up and said bracingly, 'But you'll have the baby, anyway.'

'Yes. And this.' Paula made a large gesture that took in the house and grounds. 'Oh, Verity, I still can't believe it. If only Simon could be here to share it all.'

'I wonder why he didn't like it here? Did he ever say?' Verity asked, to divert her thoughts.

'Not really. I don't think he got on very well with his father. Something happened when Simon was at university and there was a terrible row, and they were both so stubborn that neither would forgive the other. Something stupid like that. Isn't quarrelling among families the most idiotic thing to do?'

'Definitely,' Verity agreed. 'Look, there are some horses in that field over there; let's go and say hello to them.'

They walked slowly over, Paula again saying how patient and understanding Sebastian had been, so that Verity felt even more inclined to believe him when he came to collect her at five o'clock that afternoon. The day was very much like yesterday, the sun strong still, but low in the autumn sky.

'Have you ever driven a vehicle like this?' Sebastian asked her as they left the house, gesturing to the Land Rover he had been driving last evening.

Verity shook her head. 'No, they don't have much call for farm vehicles in central London.'

He grinned and opened the driver's door. 'Have a try.'

'OK.' Verity stepped up into the vehicle and settled herself in the seat, looking around with interest and trying out the gear lever.

'No qualms?' Sebastian asked as he climbed in beside her.

'I imagine it's much like any other car once you get used to it: brake, gears and accelerator. That's basically what all cars are. And I like trying out new things, having new experiences.'

'Good. Let's go for a ride up to the entrance and back first, then, shall we?'

Verity started the engine and drove confidently enough once she'd mastered the much lighter clutch and steering. 'Wow, this is much more powerful than my car, yet it's lighter to handle.'

'Probably because it has power-assisted steering. You're doing very well,' Sebastian said approvingly.

They turned at the entrance gate and drove back down the long driveway, Verity putting her foot down as she enjoyed the power under her hands.

Sebastian laughed, but said warningly, 'Watch the cattle-grid.'

She slowed down and drove at a more sedate pace up to the house, then turned to him with a happy grin. 'I enjoyed that.'

'I thought you did. Let's drive over to the bridge now.'

Her smile faded as she remembered why they were here. 'You want me to drive?'

'Yes, I think that's only fair, don't you?'

He spoke lightly, but his eyes were regarding her with steady seriousness. Slowly Verity nodded and let in the clutch. 'How fast do you think you were driving yesterday?'

'Not very fast, only about twenty-five miles an hour. And I slowed down as I came to the bridge because it's so narrow.'

They swung on to the track leading to the bridge and immediately the sun hit her in the eyes. Verity blinked and instinctively reached to pull down the sunvisor. It helped, but she still had to squint hard to see. 'Tell me when you slowed down.'

'All right. In another fifty yards or so.' He paused, sitting half turned towards her, but looking through the windscreen. 'About now.'

Verity slowed, but as she steered the Land Rover a little to the left to drive on to the bridge the sun was fully in her eyes, completely dazzling her, and she half lifted her hand to shade them. Suddenly they were out of the sun and into the deep shade of the tree, but her eyes couldn't adjust to the change immediately. She blinked hard and at the same moment became aware of a figure on the bridge. With a gasping cry, Verity swung the wheel over and stood on the brakes, but knew that she had hit whoever had been standing there.

'Oh, no!' She pulled on the handbrake and jumped out of the car to run back.

'Verity, wait!'

She heard Sebastian's voice behind her, but, full of fear and foreboding, ran to where what looked like a bundle of rags lay on the very edge of the bridge, pushed up against the rail.

It *was* a bundle of rags! When she knelt down beside it she saw that the figure was just an old coat pulled round two sacks that had been tied together and propped up with a piece of wood. Verity's first feeling was one of overwhelming relief that she hadn't hurt anyone, a relief so great that it made her feel faint. But almost immediately she realised what Sebastian had done and jumped to her feet to swing round on him in fury. 'How *could* you scare me like that? I really thought I'd hit someone!'

'Because I had to prove my point,' he said forcefully. 'Would you really have accepted my word for it that yesterday was an accident if you hadn't seen for yourself how easily it could have happened?'

He had come to stand close in front of her. Verity stared into his face as the fear gradually subsided, then turned her head away. 'You scared the hell out of me,' she told him, her voice still shaken and angry.

'I'm sorry.' Sebastian put his hands on her shoulders. 'But surely now you're convinced that I was telling the truth?'

'Oh, I'm convinced all right.' Breaking free from his hold, Verity turned her back on him and put her hands on the rail to steady herself. 'It was a terrible feeling, thinking that I'd hurt someone.'

'Yes, I know,' he replied steadily. 'That's how I felt yesterday. I'm sorry,' he repeated, 'but I felt that this was the only way to prove to you that you were mistaken. As it was, you reacted more quickly than I did; it all happened so fast that I wasn't even sure that it hadn't been a trick of the light when I hit you yesterday. It was only when I stopped and looked back that I realised that you'd gone over the bridge.' Putting his hand on her arm, he turned her to face him. 'I am most dreadfully sorry, you know,' he said, his voice low and earnest. 'Do you believe me now?'

'Yes. Yes, I believe you, but I don't think I like your method of proving your point.' She was still shaken, and thought that it had been a very drastic thing to do—almost cruel, in fact. 'I had a bad enough shock yesterday, without having you fabricate a false one today,' she said feelingly.

'It wasn't intended to be like that,' Sebastian answered with a rueful look. 'I just wanted you to realise how easily it could have happened, and I was going to tell you immediately that it was only a dummy, but you were out of the car so fast I didn't have a chance.' His hand tightened on her arm. 'I just don't seem to be able to do the right thing where you're concerned, do I?' His mouth twisted a little. 'I don't usually have this trouble.' Then he gave her such a warm smile that her heart seemed to skip a beat. 'But now that we've sorted things out, well—can you forgive me?'

It was impossible to resist that smile. Verity felt the strength of his hand on her arm, was aware of the lean hardness of his body close to hers, and of the sun dappling his features into shades of light and dark as he looked at her so intently. Her chest felt tight and suddenly it was difficult to breathe. Lowering her head, she said huskily, 'I—yes, I—I suppose so.'

An amused look came into his grey eyes. 'Such a grudging response! Are you always this wary?'

It had been grudging, she realised, and maybe he didn't deserve that. After all, he had only been trying to prove to her that the accident had just been an unfortunate chance, a set of circumstances that had combined to make a near-tragedy. A fact he had known all along, but which she had dogmatically refused to believe until he had shown her that it could easily have happened to her, too. Fully convinced now, she said generously, 'No, it's I who should apologise. I accused you of some very nasty things, when all the time you saved me from a terrible injury. If I'd fallen into the sluice; if you hadn't stopped and hauled me up...'

Her voice wavered a little and Sebastian said quickly, 'But you didn't fall.'

'No, but I ought to have been thanking you instead of accusing you of—of, well, of trying to kill me.'

'Nonsense,' Sebastian said roundly. 'Now, let's make a pact, shall we? We'll both forget that the incident ever happened and we won't mention it again. OK?'

He quirked an eyebrow at her and Verity nodded and smiled. 'OK.'

His eyes resting on her face, Sebastian said, 'You have a very lovely smile; I haven't seen it before.' Then he grinned. 'But we've agreed to forget why. I just hope that you keep smiling at me.'

'I'll try.' Feeling a little unsure of herself, Verity turned away and looked down at the river. 'Oh, look! My shawl is still down there. It fell off—yesterday,' she explained, and then laughed. 'Oh, dear, it isn't going to be so easy.'

Sebastian looked to where she pointed, but then turned away. 'Have you walked through the wood yet?

It's very pleasant at this time of the year. There's a path over here.'

Pushing his hands into his pockets, he led the way across the bridge and down the track a little way before turning on to a fairly wide path that meandered through the trees. The leaves were thick underfoot here, especially under the wide-spreading chestnut trees, their tall bare branches clutching at the sky. Verity liked the feel of them under her feet and the noise they made as she almost waded through them. Everything was so golden, so full of beauty, a beauty of which she was even more acutely aware after she had come so close to death such a short time ago. She paused to bend down and pick up a horse-chestnut, the green spiky covering partly split open. Carefully she prised off the shell and took out the new, gleaming chestnut, its skin a beautiful, burnished copper.

'It's the colour of your hair,' Sebastian said lightly, watching her.

She smiled. 'I have a very dim memory of playing conkers when I was a child. I seem to remember we went to spend a day in the country and my father filled his pockets full of them for me. I took them to school and we played conkers at every free moment until the last one split.'

She paused, her eyes becoming sad, then suddenly turned and flung the chestnut away from her as far and as hard as she could.

'Was it that unhappy a memory?' Sebastian asked, his eyes on her.

Verity kicked some leaves out of the way and began to walk on before saying, 'No, but sometimes it's happy memories that hurt.'

She didn't say anything more. Sebastian walked beside her and for some time they strolled along in silence, Verity full of her own thoughts, until Sebastian said, 'You and Paula seem very close. Have you known each other long?'

'For almost exactly fifteen years.' She paused, wondering whether to tell him, but felt somehow that she wanted to, although usually she made a point of not talking about her past in case people got the wrong idea and thought she was looking for sympathy. 'Our fathers worked for the same international company. They were civil engineers and had just finished building a hydro-electric dam out in the Philippines somewhere. When it was opened our mothers were flown out there by the company to take part in the celebrations.' Her mouth twisted as she said, 'It was a reward for the great job our fathers had done. The highlight of the trip was to be a flight over the dam so that they could see it from the air. They all went up in the plane, all four of them, and some other European employees and their wives. But the plane developed engine trouble and crashed into the dam. They were all killed. Ironic, wasn't it?'

She paused, half expecting Sebastian to say something, to offer his unwanted condolences perhaps, but he was silent, waiting for her to go on, and presently she said, 'Paula and I had no other relatives, no one to look after us, so the company took over as our legal guardians and sent us to a boarding-school. That's where we met and that's why we're close and always will be.'

'So you're like sisters,' Sebastian commented.

'Closer than sisters, perhaps, because there's no sibling rivalry. We needed each other. After we left school we went to the same college, and then shared a flat until Paula went to Bahrain and met Simon.'

Sebastian came to a stop and leaned back against a tree trunk, his eyes on her face. 'Did that upset you?'

Verity laughed delightedly. 'Good heavens, no! I thought it was marvellous. I regarded Simon almost as a brother-in-law, a third member of our family. Did you think I was jealous?' She laughed again. 'Have you looked at Paula? She's beautiful, and she has that fragile, helpless air; she's the sort of girl that men always want to marry and protect.'

His mouth quirking in amusement, Sebastian said, 'And how about you? Are you the same?'

She raised her eyebrows at him. 'Of course not, I'm too tall. How can a man protect a girl he has to look up to?'

Sebastian gave a laugh of rich, masculine amusement. 'Being tall myself, it hadn't occurred to me. There are very few women I even see eye to eye with. But you're not against marriage?'

She shook her head, slightly confused by the question. 'In principle, no.'

'But in practice?'

Her cheeks slightly flushed, Verity said, 'Shall we say that I haven't yet met anyone I care to put the principle into practice with.'

'Beautifully put,' Sebastian said with a grin. His eyes, still full of amusement, lingered on her face.

'And how about you?' she asked, feeling that she could do so now.

'Oh, I'm the same as you.' Sebastian straightened up. 'Still waiting for the right girl to come along.'

'You mean you're still playing the field, huh?'

'Right again,' he grinned. They began to walk on, but after a moment Sebastian said, 'And do you think that Paula will marry again—once she's got over Simon, of course?'

Verity hesitated, but then said, 'Yes, I'm sure she will. She needs a man, someone to look after her, and even more so when she has the baby. Being orphaned made her feel very insecure, you see.'

Sebastian gave her a swift look. 'And that's why you came here with her?'

Verity nodded. 'Yes, that's why I came.'

'Paula is lucky to have a friend who's willing to do so much for her.'

She sensed rather than heard an ironic note in his voice and immediately said defensively, 'Paula would do exactly the same for me if I needed her.'

Sebastian held up his hands in a gesture of surrender. 'OK, don't shoot me down. I was simply rather envious, that's all.'

'Envious?'

'Yes, such loyal friendships must be almost unique nowadays—platonic friendships, anyway. It's probably because it began when you were children, and in such special circumstances,' Sebastian said musingly. 'And because you're the same sex, of course; I don't think you could ever get such a close platonic friendship between a man and a woman.'

'Especially if they were each married to someone else,' Verity agreed. 'The partner would be bound to be jealous and not understand.'

'Or else understand, but want all the person's love for her or himself,' Sebastian added drily.

Verity gave him a swift look, wondering what personal experience he had had to bring bitterness to his tone. Abruptly, Sebastian changed the subject and began to talk about the garden as they emerged from the trees on the other side of the wood. 'A very old oak tree came down over there in last year's big storm,' he said, pointing to an uneven dip in the ground about a hundred yards nearer the house. 'It took a time to clear away and I was going to plant a new young tree, but then we heard that Paula was pregnant and I thought we might wait until the baby is born and plant the tree on the same day. Do you think Paula would like that?'

'I'm quite sure she would.' Verity turned a glowing face to him. 'In fact, I know she'd love it. It's very thoughtful of you. When are you going to tell her?'

He gave a slight shrug. 'Why don't you tell her?'

'Oh, but I'm sure she'd prefer to hear all about it from you, as it's your idea,' Verity protested, thinking that it would help to make Paula feel that she was really welcome here, and not only her but the baby, too. Thoughts of the baby made her say curiously, 'You must love this place.'

'It's very beautiful,' Sebastian admitted, which didn't tell her anything at all.

'It's such a shame that Simon didn't bring Paula here before,' she pursued, trying another approach. She waited, hopefully, for Sebastian to say something, but when he didn't had to say rather lamely, 'Of course, he was always very busy, establishing and expanding his business in Bahrain.'

'Oh, yes, I'm quite sure he found plenty of excuses—I beg his pardon—reasons for not coming back here.' And this time there was definite sarcasm in Sebastian's voice.

'You didn't like Simon, did you?' Verity said with certainty.

Thrusting his hands deep into his pockets, he said shortly, 'We certainly didn't have the same relationship as you and Paula have, if that's what you mean.'

'It isn't what I mean. You sound as if you had no time at all for him.'

He gave a short laugh. 'Simon was a spoilt brat; his father doted on him, my mother was too soft with him because she was afraid of being called a wicked stepmother, and the staff, the people in the village, and the neighbours all pandered to him because he was the heir.'

'And you?' Verity ventured.

He didn't speak for a long moment and she thought that she had ventured too far into his privacy, but at length Sebastian said, 'Oh, I was as bad as the rest, I suppose. I enjoyed having a younger brother, and he had very charming manners. Trouble was, he was just too charming for his own good.'

There was finality in his tone, and Verity didn't dare to question him further, but she found the few things that he had said absolutely intriguing. She hadn't known Simon Layton at all well herself, only having met him when he'd come over to England to see Paula a few times before he'd persuaded her to marry him, and then again at the wedding. Later she had gone over to Bahrain to spend a holiday with them, although even then she hadn't seen much of Simon because he had been away on business most of the time. But she had always liked him; he had been one of those people that one took an instinctive liking to and went on liking even when one had discovered their faults. Only Simon Layton hadn't lived long enough for her to find out any of his faults. Fleetingly she wondered if Paula had in their two years of marriage, but Paula had adored Simon, and was close to so few people that she refused to admit that anyone she loved had any faults at all. She was, too, the type to bring out the best in people, so if Simon had had a callow side he would probably never have shown it to her.

She pushed the thoughts out of her mind as they walked back, Sebastian telling her something of the history of the house. She listened for any proprietorial note in his voice, but there was none; he spoke of the place as if he had read up on its history and found it interesting, nothing more. There was no love in his voice, no regret that he might have to hand it all over to someone else. His tone was very dispassionate, very controlled. Too controlled, perhaps?

He was very unlike Simon, she thought. The younger man had been far more excitable, given to sudden whims and intense, almost obsessive interests. Like his interest in sailing, and camel racing, although that hadn't lasted very long, according to Paula. Verity stole a glance at Sebastian and thought that she definitely hadn't liked him on sight—quite the opposite, in fact—but she felt somehow that he had far more depth to his character than Simon could ever have had. If she could get to know him well enough for him to open up and let her find out. And suddenly her heart warmed as she realised that she would very much like to get to know him very well indeed.

# CHAPTER FOUR

FROM that hour everything seemed to change for the better at Layton House. Paula was far more relaxed now that she had had the talk with Sebastian and knew where she stood regarding the house and estate. And Verity couldn't believe that she'd been such a fool. Her feelings about Sebastian were completely reversed, but strangely she kept the fact to herself, only telling Paula that he had proved to her that she had most probably been mistaken. In the past Verity had confided everything to her friend, and the fact that she wasn't being completely open now rather surprised her. And embarrassed her a little, too. She wasn't usually the secretive type, but somehow this change of feeling towards Sebastian was something she wanted to keep to herself; it was so new, so unexpected, and as yet so tentative. And she had no real idea how he felt about her.

The atmosphere over the next few days was far more agreeable and relaxed. Sebastian was usually out on business during the day, but he was home for dinner every evening and at the weekend, and although Verity was seldom alone with him for any length of time she felt that she was getting to know more about him, and liking all that she learnt. Maggie, too, was always helpful and kind, so Mrs Chivers' sour attitude was the only detraction. Paula had met her now, and agreed with Verity that the woman was an old grouch. And her husband was as bad, if not worse. The girls ran into him one morning when they were returning from a walk round the garden and passed the garage. A man in working clothes came out carrying a box of tools, hesitated when he saw them, then went to walk past. But Paula stopped and said, 'Good morning. You must be Mr Chivers,' with one of her nicest smiles. But the man just gave her a glowering look and went right past them without saying a word.

'Well, really!' Paula stared after him, unable to credit such downright rudeness. 'What on earth's the matter with him?'

'If you'd been married to Mrs Chivers half your life you might be miserable, too,' Verity suggested with a grin.

'Or it could be the other way round; maybe it's Mr Chivers who's made his wife miserable.'

'Well, whichever it is there's nothing you can do about it until the place becomes yours,' Verity reminded her. 'So there doesn't seem to be much point in worrying about them. Let Maggie cope; she seems to do it very well.'

'I'll never understand why she keeps them on, though. They're so surly. Surely staff can't be that hard to get, not when you're offering them a cottage as well?'

There was a trace of anxiety for the future in Paula's tone, so Verity said soothingly, 'No, I'm sure you won't have any difficulty. I think Maggie just keeps them on out of kindness, or out of habit because they've been here such a long time.'

'Well, I don't care how long they've been here, the first thing I'm going to do after the baby is born is to ask them to leave,' Paula said with determination.

'Good for you,' Verity agreed. She turned to watch Mr Chivers striding along in the direction of the bridge and his cottage, a puzzled look in her eyes. 'But you'd think they'd realise that their jobs depend on you and that they'd make an effort to at least be civil.'

'Perhaps it's country pride or something,' Paula suggested. 'A dislike of anyone new, especially if they come from London. I've read about that kind of thing.' She turned away impatiently. 'Oh, let's forget about them. Do you really think we could decorate the nursery ourselves?'

'No, but I think I could decorate it while you supervise,' Verity corrected her. 'You're in no condition to be running up and down ladders, so don't you dare try it.'

'Well, if you're sure. But there's quite a lot of work involved, you know.'

'But you're not expecting the baby for three months; even I can decorate one room in three months.'

'All right, but I really need to go through colour charts and get material samples and that kind of thing before I finally decide what I want.'

'OK, so we'll ask Maggie where the nearest town is and then drive over there.'

But Maggie went out to dinner and to play bridge with friends that evening, so it was Sebastian who gave them the information. 'The nearest town of any size is Melford. Tell you what, Paula has an appointment with the family solicitor there tomorrow morning. Why don't I run you both in and I can show Verity where the shops she needs are while Paula keeps her appointment? Then perhaps we could have lunch in the town.'

'That sounds fine,' Paula said enthusiastically. 'That's OK with you, isn't it, Verity?'

'Yes, of course. Thank you.' She smiled at Sebastian and he smiled back, but then his glance moved on to encompass Paula too, and Verity felt an irrational little stab of jealousy which went as quickly as it came.

There was a sharp frost the next morning, the first of the autumn, but by the time they left for Melford in Sebastian's Jaguar the frost had melted in the sun and the day was bright and warm. There was a moment of hiatus before they left when he opened the back door of the car and glanced towards them. Paula got in and Verity hesitated for a second, wondering whether he expected her to get in the back too, but Sebastian firmly shut the door and opened the front passenger one for her. They chatted sociably enough as they drove along, the girls now far more at ease with him, but Verity found that she was looking forward to the time when they dropped Paula off at the solicitor's office and they would be alone.

Melford proved to be a pretty and comparatively unspoilt market town with a wide high street and mostly eighteenth-century buildings above the shop fronts. Only one brash supermarket, its windows full of discount posters, had managed to intrude itself into the pleasant aspect. Sebastian drove almost to the end of the street and turned into a driveway at the side of a large Georgian house, that had obviously been turned into offices, and parked in the paved area at the back.

'The solicitor's is only a short way from here,' he told them.

'This isn't their building, then?' Verity remarked.

'No, I have an office here myself.'

Sebastian didn't say anything more and Verity didn't feel that she could come right out and ask what he did. He walked with them down the street and Verity waited outside while he took Paula in to introduce her to the solicitor. He was gone for only a few minutes, and when he came out said, 'I think Paula will be at least an hour, if not more. Now, there's a comparatively new shop in the town that does wallpaper with matching materials that I think might have what you want. It's across the road.'

They walked to the kerb and Sebastian put a protective hand under her elbow as they crossed the road. There had been a time, in the feminist days of her teens, when Verity would have resented that gesture and told the person with her that she was as capable of crossing the road without help as he was. But today she felt not feminism, but femininity, and accepted his assistance quite naturally, liking the feel of his hand on her arm.

The next hour went all too quickly. They visited the shop Sebastian had suggested, and, although it had nothing like the comprehensive range and service they would have found in London, they took away swatches of material and wallpaper samples for Paula to choose from, then went to a do-it-yourself shop for paint charts. Several times Verity asked Sebastian his opinion and he gave it readily enough, displaying a taste that strongly coincided with her own. They looked through the charts together, their heads close, and it was impossible not to be aware of him. Verity glanced up and caught sight of their reflected images in a mirror on the wall; they looked right together, she thought, and wondered for a fanciful moment what it would be like if they were choosing materials to decorate somewhere of their own.

'What do you think of this one?' She didn't answer and Sebastian looked up and saw her looking in the mirror. 'Hey, you're miles away.'

'Oh, yes, sorry.' She coloured a little and his eyebrows rose, but she quickly said, 'Yes, I like that,' and hoped that the moment had passed.

Sebastian glanced at his watch. 'Well, if you've got everything you want, I think we have time to walk to the park and see our famous castle before we collect Paula.'

As they strolled through the town they passed several antique shops and Verity couldn't resist looking in the windows.

'You're obviously keen on antiques,' Sebastian observed as she looked into the third window. 'Do you like antiques in general or anything in particular?'

'I collect teapots,' she admitted. 'I've got quite a collection at home, but the first and nicest one is a teapot that I inherited from my grandmother. Nearly everything else was sold when my parents were killed, but that was put in store for me until I was eighteen. I like other antiques too, of course, especially furniture, but the teapots are about as much as I can afford after paying the mortgage, and they look good on my Welsh dresser.'

Sebastian was interested and asked her several questions, then flicked his fingers in remembrance as he said, 'Got it! I knew I'd read something about teapots recently and I've been trying to remember. Seeing that auction notice outside the estate agents has reminded me. There's a country house sale coming up in a few weeks. I think it's in Longchester, which is about thirty or so miles from here. And I'm sure I read that there's a large collection of china. How would you like to go? There might be something there that would interest you.'

'Why, yes, I'd 'ike to very much. I haven't been to a house sale before.'

'Good.' Sebastian smiled at her. 'I'll make sure of the date and let you know. Perhaps we could make a day of it.'

She smiled in return, her eyes bright now that she was sure he intended to go with her. 'I'd like that very much. Thank you.'

They walked on, then stopped to look in the window of a picture gallery, so they talked mostly about the arts as they sauntered through the park in the sun. Sebastian chatted easily on the subject and knew what he was talking about, but he didn't have Verity's advantage of living in London and being able to go to art galleries and the theatre every time there was a new exhibition or a new play, so he wasn't so up to date. Many men might have dropped the subject then, not liking to be at a disadvantage, but Sebastian was plainly pleased that she was so knowledgeable and listened with interest to her descriptions and opinion.

Verity found her steps slowing and she began to wish that they didn't have to meet Paula. She felt so much more in accord with Sebastian than any man she'd met in a long time. Living and working in London, she had never been short of dates; there had been many men who had been attracted by her good looks and shining intelligence, and several who wanted a more permanent relationship. But all the men that Verity met were heavily into their careers, and she always had the feeling that, although they might care for her a great deal, with them work would always come first. Perhaps she was being selfish or even unrealistic, but Verity felt that any man she loved would always come first with her and he ought to feel that way, too. Sebastian was describing a Turner exhibition he'd been to, but as she listened, her eyes on his face, Verity's thoughts wandered. He was so different from most of the men she knew; they would have told her their name coupled with their career, as if the two were permanently linked, but she had lived in the same house as Sebastian for over a week and yet had only just found out that he had an office in Melford—and she still didn't know what he did there. He was very self-possessed, too, although she had an idea that he had a ruthless streak hidden away somewhere. And she liked the way his hair curled slightly where it met his collar, and the hard, clean-cut line of his jaw, and the way his mouth twisted a little when he smiled, and——

'Here we are.' Sebastian broke into her thoughts as he gestured towards some stone ruins. 'The castle—or rather the remains of it.'

The castle was in the middle of the park and turned out to be more infamous than famous, having been the home of a particularly brutal nobleman in medieval times who seemed to take great delight in persecuting the local population. There wasn't a great deal of it left now, just the gatehouse and the remains of a keep and a few towers. They walked round them as Sebastian described the way in which the townsfolk had finally turned on their oppressor. He told the story well, making her laugh as she listened to him, but then he broke off unexpectedly and she saw his face sharpen with tension. They had just emerged from the keep and he was looking ahead, down the path that led back to the town. Verity automatically turned to see what had caught his attention, but he took her arm and quite deliberately turned to go in the other direction, continuing the story as if nothing had happened, but lengthening his stride so that she had to walk smartly to keep up.

But they had only gone a few yards when a voice, a young, female voice, called, 'Sebastian!' and when he took no notice repeated his name insistently.

'I think someone's calling you,' Verity pointed out.

He gave her a strange kind of look and his mouth thinned. Reluctantly he stopped and they turned to wait for the girl to come up to them. She was probably in her late twenties, a few years older than Verity, but shorter and with a more curvaceous figure. Her hair was blonde, but it had a metallic glint in the sun, showing that it had had help from a bottle, and she wore a short, tight red leather skirt, thigh-high boots, and a long, figure-hugging sweater. The girl was a little out of breath from hurrying and there was a glint of triumph in her heavily made-up eyes. Verity decided that she disliked her on sight.

'Why, Sebastian, what a lovely surprise! It's ages since we met.' The girl's voice was throaty, but she spoke slowly, as if she studied each word before she spoke, like someone speaking a foreign language. 'How are you?'

'Well enough.' In comparison Sebastian's voice was harsh and decidedly curt. 'I'm afraid you'll have to excuse us, we're meeting someone.'

The girl gave a tinkling laugh. 'My, my, what a rush. But I won't keep you.' But she came nearer and, putting a familiar hand on his arm, looked up into his face. 'Besides you always know where to find me, Sebastian, sweetie. Just as I know where to find you, don't I?'

The grip on Verity's arm tightened so much that she winced, and Sebastian's brows gathered into a dark, angry frown as he turned on his heel and strode briskly away, pulling Verity along with him. Behind them they heard the girl laugh again, a sound that somehow seemed to hold a threat in it, but Sebastian didn't turn or stop until they were out of the park.

He slowed down then and Verity said sharply, 'Can I have my arm back now?'

'What? Oh, sorry.' And he let her go.

'Thanks!' She rubbed her arm and turned her head away from him, trying to hide the disappointment in her eyes. That nasty little scene with the girl in the park had been enlightening and all too obvious. She had spoken so familiarly that she could be nothing but an old flame, and one that he was evidently ashamed of, at that. That the girl was a man-trap was clear from the way she dressed and the way she looked at him, but Verity didn't see that that gave Sebastian the right to treat her like dirt or try to ignore her. But what hurt most was that he had lowered his standards enough to get involved with that type of girl in the first place. It made Verity's own growing liking for him somehow feel cheapened and dirty.

They walked back to the solicitor's office faster than they need have done, neither of them finding anything to say. Sebastian still had an angry frown on his face and was obviously preoccupied with his own harsh thoughts. It wasn't until they met Paula again that he made an attempt to hide his annoyance and be sociable.

'I've booked a table at the Red Lion,' he told them as he ushered them out of the solicitor's. 'It's over there, on the other side of the market square.' He pointed as he spoke and they both obediently looked in that direction, but as Verity's gaze swept round a glint of blonde caught at the corner of her vision. Quickly she looked back and saw the girl they had met in the park. She was standing on the other side of the road, partly hidden by a queue of people who were waiting for a bus, but not a part of it, almost as if she had deliberately tried to conceal herself. If it hadn't been for the sun shining on that impossibly bright hair Verity wouldn't have noticed her; Sebastian certainly hadn't, he was talking to Paula. She wondered why the girl was standing there watching them, but Sebastian and Paula had started to walk towards the pub and she had to turn away and catch them up.

The Red Lion was a large inn right in the centre of the town, with a pleasant panelled dining-room with hunting prints on the walls and Georgian bow-fronted windows looking out on to the street. But first they had a drink in the bar where Sebastian handed them menus to choose from.

'I think you'll find the food plain, but good,' he told them.

Verity reached up to take hers from him and their hands touched fleetingly. 'Sorry.' She quickly drew her hand back, then glanced up and caught his eye. He began to smile at her, but she deliberately looked away and began to study the menu. Sebastian sat back, his face hardening and his mouth setting into a grim line.

Luckily Paula didn't seem to notice anything amiss; she was bright and lively today, and full of interest for the samples they'd collected.

'I'm afraid there wasn't a huge selection to choose from,' Verity apologised. 'They could do with a really good interior designer in this town.'

'I'm sure we'll find something,' Paula assured her. 'I've never designed a nursery before; it will be fun.'

Verity smiled at her friend, pleased that she seemed happy. Paula didn't mention her meeting at the solicitor's during lunch, but it must obviously have reassured her or she wouldn't have been so relaxed. And because Paula was in such a good mood Verity tried hard to put her own thoughts out of her mind and be cheerful, too. They were shown to a table in one of the windows, the sun slanting down through the little bull's-eye panes and making weird patterns on the white tablecloth. As Sebastian had said, the food was very good. The inn specialised in home-made pies with crusts so light that they rose a couple of inches from the dish. 'Mmm, lovely!' Paula exclaimed. 'I feel so *hungry* today!' A remark which was so deep with feeling that they all laughed, and that helped to relieve the feeling of constraint between Verity and Sebastian.

'This looks such a nice town,' Paula went on. 'I'm looking forward to exploring it properly. Did you manage to see much of it with Sebastian?'

'Quite a bit. There's a very old castle with quite an interesting history,' Verity said drily. 'You must get Sebastian to tell you about it some time. He tells it very well.' She glanced at him as she spoke and saw a sardonic look come into his eyes.

'I shall certainly do that, then,' Paula said with a smile. 'And I must go and see it, too. Where is it? Far from here?'

'No, just through the park. Only about ten minutes' walk away.' Sebastian pointed out of the window, but then grew still, his eyes on the street. Verity looked out and saw what he had seen. The girl was there again. She was walking slowly along the pavement below, her head turned towards the inn so that she looked directly at them. When she saw them looking towards her she threw back her head and laughed. They couldn't hear her through the window, of course, but Verity felt that unnatural laugh jangling in her ears. The girl continued to look at them for a moment, then, obviously satisfied that they'd seen her, quickened her pace and walked out of sight.

Paula was following Sebastian's directing finger and hadn't noticed anything, but Sebastian knew that Verity had seen. He turned to look at her, his eyes holding hers steadily, as if daring her to put any interpretation on it. Her chin came up and the air between them was suddenly alive with tension. But then Verity dropped her eyes; it was none of her business, and she had too much concern for her own privacy not to respect his.

They talked of other things, but as soon as the meal was over Sebastian said he was sorry, but he had to meet someone that afternoon, and drove them back to Layton House. He dropped them off at the entrance gate, and as soon as he'd driven away Paula began to talk about her meeting with the solicitor, saying, 'Everything is exactly as Sebastian said it was, right down to the last detail. And the solicitor told me how marvellously Sebastian has looked after the estate, even before Simon's father died. He said that it had become far more efficient since he took it over.'

'Did you ask him whether Sebastian drew a salary?' Verity asked curiously.

'No, he doesn't. Just expenses.'

'I wonder what he does in his office in Melford, then?'

'Why don't you ask him?'

Verity shrugged. 'Oh, I'm not really interested, it was just passing curiosity.'

'Liar. I've an idea you're quite attracted to Sebastian,' Paula teased.

Verity's face shadowed. 'Somehow I don't think that would be a very good idea.'

'What do you mean?' Paula demanded, immediately picking up the dry note in her voice.

For a moment Verity hesitated, wondering whether to tell Paula what had happened. Perhaps she shouldn't—after all, it was only surmise on her part, and it wasn't really their concern. But her own inner disappointment was so great that she had to tell someone, so she said, 'Because I met one of Sebastian's old flames today.'

'Really?' Paula's elegantly arched eyebrows rose. 'Well, go on, you can't just stop there.'

'She looked—cheap. Peroxide and leather. You know the type I mean.'

Paula stared at her. 'Sebastian? Going out with someone like that? I just don't see it.'

'Nor would I have done. Still, there's no knowing how people get their kicks. You only have to read the tabloids to find out how perverted some men are.'

'Yes, but Sebastian...'

'I know.'

They both fell silent until Paula said, 'Are you sure she was an old flame?'

'She called him "sweetie".'

'Yeuk! I'd love to have seen her. Was she really ghastly?'

'No.' Verity felt a sudden surge of anger. 'She was just brought up differently and doesn't know any better, I suppose. And who are we to criticise, anyway? And Sebastian evidently fancied her at some point, although he couldn't get away fast enough this morning. He even tried to ignore her.'

Paula gave her a swift look. 'Perhaps he didn't want to own up to his—weakness in front of you.'

'Oh, I'm quite sure he didn't. He was obviously ashamed of even knowing her. But I'd have admired him more if he'd had the courage to face up to her instead of trying to run away.'

'It's strange,' Paula said musingly. 'I'd never have put Sebastian down as the type who was afraid to stand up to anything.'

'No,' Verity agreed, her voice heavy. 'Nor would I—until now.' They were both silent, thinking their own thoughts, until Verity said, 'And I don't think he could have handled the affair very well, because after she saw us in the park the girl followed us, and then walked by when we were having lunch in the inn. I think she did it deliberately to try to embarrass Sebastian.'

'Really? I didn't see her.' Paula's steps slowed as she looked at Verity. 'And was he embarrassed?'

'No, I don't think it was embarrassment he felt,' Verity said with a frown. 'He was angry, mostly. And he didn't make any attempt to be even civil to her.'

Paula's delicate nose wrinkled in distaste. 'It all sounds rather nasty.'

'Yes, it was,' Verity agreed. 'But you'd think Sebastian would be experienced enough to know how to end an affair without making an enemy of the girl.'

'Yes. Do you think he's very experienced?' Paula asked speculatively.

They looked at each other, then grinned. 'That was a very feminine question.'

'Yes, wasn't it?' Paula agreed. She paused and then said, 'I think I might go up to London one day soon and buy myself some maternity outfits.'

'Am I invited along?'

'Of course. But my old boss at the interior design company has invited me to have lunch with him the next time I'm in town.'

'Well, that works out all right, because it will give me a chance to go to my house and make sure it's still OK.' Verity glanced at Paula and smiled. 'You're starting to come alive again.'

'Am I? I must admit I feel better now that I don't have to worry about the house and estate any more. It's wonderful to know that the baby's future is taken care of. And Maggie has been so kind. And Sebastian. And you, of course.' She put her hand on Verity's arm. 'That goes without saying.'

'And you know you don't have to say it. But thanks anyway.' An idea came to her and she said, 'When we're in London we can go and look at those nursery wallpapers I was telling you about; the selection in Melford wasn't nearly as good. They really need a good design shop there that covers all aspects of decorating. Sebastian said that there isn't one in any of the surrounding towns, either, just shops that special-

ise in different parts of the trade, like curtain-making
or selling ceramic tiles.'

'Really?' Paula gave her a pensive look and became
lost in her own thoughts for the rest of the walk to
the house.

They decided to go up to London a week or so later,
on a Monday, when the shops wouldn't be too
crowded, and to stay overnight at Verity's house.

'Perhaps I ought to have my car checked over before
we go, though,' Verity remarked as they discussed it
over dinner one day. 'I don't want it to break down
again.'

'Why don't you go by train?' Maggie suggested. 'It
would be less tiring for both of you. There's a very
good express service from Melford. And Sebastian
could run you to the station and pick you up.'

'I think the train's a good idea,' Verity agreed. 'But
we can quite easily take a taxi. There's no need for
Sebastian to bother.'

He was sitting at the end of the table to her left
and gave her a look of amused irony. 'It's really no
trouble. And we certainly don't want Paula standing
around in the cold waiting for a taxi to turn up, now
do we?'

Verity bit her lip, recognising the challenge in his
tone, but refusing to meet it. Since the trip to Melford
there had been restraint between them and they had
lost the growing friendliness. That it was her fault
Verity knew, but somehow she couldn't get the idea
of Sebastian with the girl in the park out of her mind.
Her feelings about him were so mixed up; from a terrible start of fear and suspicion she had quickly gone
to liking him very much, and added to that liking was
a growing sexual attraction that she found hard to

resist. But it had been a shock to find that Sebastian was so fallible, that he could be seduced by such an obvious and flashy sex-kitten. It had lowered him in her estimation—and yet she still felt attracted to him, which made her angry with herself and so with him.

Maggie was a bridge fanatic; she played regularly twice a week, on Tuesdays and Fridays, at the homes of various neighbours, and often had friends round for a game at the weekend. She had been delighted to find that the girls knew how to play the game, although their standard was far below hers, and they often played for an hour or so in the evenings. She suggested a game that evening, and they sat round the card-table, Verity opposite Sebastian, whom she'd drawn as a partner. He was a good player and never got angry if his partner made a mistake, willing to point out where they'd gone wrong if asked, but not one of those players who found it necessary to hold an inquest after every hand. Which was just as well, because Verity didn't play at all well that night.

The card-table was an antique, and rather smaller than the standard size. Both she and Sebastian were tall and, being a man, he liked to stretch out his legs. They had been playing only a short while when Verity unthinkingly crossed her legs under the table and they brushed against his. She quickly drew back, but her colour heightened, and when she looked at Sebastian under her lashes she saw a look of mocking amusement in his eyes. This only made her even more aware of him, and she found it almost impossible to concentrate when she had to look at him, meet his eyes, talk to him, in the course of the game.

'You seem quite preoccupied tonight, Verity,' Maggie remarked. 'You just trumped Sebastian's ace.'

'Oh! Did I? Sorry.' The apology was addressed to Sebastian, but she didn't look at him, instead putting down her cards, thankful that the rubber was over. 'I think I need some fresh air. If you'll excuse me, I think I'll go for a walk.'

After going upstairs to fetch her coat, Verity let herself out of the front door and walked slowly through the garden, her hands thrust into her pockets. It was a beautiful night, the stars clear and bright in the crisp coolness of the sky. Without making any conscious decision, she began to walk past the house and along the track leading to the bridge. The river was fascinating and mysterious in the moonlight, bubbling like molten silver over rocks and swirling into dark, secret pools under overhanging trees. She stood there, leaning against the rail, letting her thoughts flow with the river.

The footsteps sounded quite clearly in the still night, coming towards her along the track from the direction of the house, and she instinctively knew that it was Sebastian. She turned to face him, her hand on the rail, and he stopped in a patch of moonlight, a couple of yards away. 'Just so that you realise it's me and don't start hollering blue murder,' he said wryly.

'I've already admitted I was wrong about that.'

He came nearer. 'But it hasn't stopped you from jumping to conclusions a second time, has it?'

'I don't know what you mean.'

'Yes, you do. You saw that girl who spoke to me in the park and immediately put a completely wrong interpretation on it. That's why you've been avoiding me ever since.'

'I haven't been avoiding you,' Verity said defensively. 'How could I avoid you when we're living in the same house?'

'With difficulty—but you've had a darn good try.' He gave an impatient gesture. 'Look, you've been wrong about me once; didn't it occur to you that you might be wrong again?' She was silent and he said harshly, 'Didn't you have any reservations?'

'It all seemed so—obvious.' Verity turned her head away. 'The way that girl looked at you, spoke to you, and—and touched you.'

'Maybe that was because it was meant to look obvious.'

She turned, puzzled. 'I don't understand.'

Sebastian gave an angry sigh. 'Sometimes people have enemies. She's one of ours.'

'Ours?'

'Mine, then.' He waited for her to speak, but when she didn't, said, 'Don't you want to know why?'

Stiffly, Verity said, 'It's really none of my business. I don't have the right to ask.'

'Then damn well give yourself the right,' Sebastian said in sudden anger.

'How?' She faced up to him, her own feelings rising. 'I can't just——'

'Yes, you can! Like this.' And, stepping forward, he pulled her roughly into his arms and kissed her.

As first kisses went, it wasn't exactly romantic. There was no soft gentleness, no tender emotions growing into desire. Sebastian's lips were hard and overbearing. He held her imprisoned in his arms and bent her back under the force of his mouth, taking everything and giving nothing. But when he finally let her go and stepped back she definitely knew that she'd been kissed.

'Now,' he said, his voice unsteady. 'Now you have the right.'

But Verity couldn't find anything to say. Her heart was hammering in her chest and her throat felt too tight, too constricted for any words to come out. Her knees felt weak and she leaned back against the rail, but Sebastian quickly put his hand out to grab her arm.

'I don't want you going over the rail again.'

Huskily she said, 'Don't you?'

'No.' He looked into her face for a moment, then kissed her again, and it was far better this time. Verity even got a chance to put her arms round his neck.

'So who is that girl?' she asked when he eventually let her go.

Sebastian grinned. 'I see you get your priorities right. She used to work here some years ago, but she was—a troublemaker, and we had to get rid of her. But I'm afraid she still bears a grudge against us. Unfortunately her people still live near here and, although she's away most of the time, she occasionally comes back and tries to annoy us.'

'Can't you stop her?'

He shrugged and bent to lean on the rail. 'Ignoring her is by far the best method.' He glanced at her. 'That way she's unable to give people the wrong impression.'

Verity caught the sardonic note in his voice and said, 'Why didn't you tell me straight off?'

'I prefer to forget her. But I would have done if I'd known the effect it was going to have on you.'

'It didn't have any effect on me,' Verity protested.

Sebastian laughed and straightened up. 'If you say so, of course. But I must admit that I was hoping you were just a tiny bit jealous.'

'Certainly not.' But then she smiled. 'Not jealous, that wasn't how I felt.'

'No?' But he didn't question her further, instead kissing her again before putting an arm across her shoulders as they began to walk back to the house. 'Did you mention anything about the girl to Paula?' he asked a few moments later.

Verity nodded. 'Yes, I did. Does it matter?'

'Not really, I suppose. I just thought that it might be better to keep anything at all unpleasant from her at the moment. We don't want her to take an irrational dislike to the place, do we? Women can do that, I understand, when they're pregnant.'

'No, we don't,' Verity agreed. 'I'm sorry I told her now.'

'What woman could resist?' he said teasingly. 'But perhaps you could play it down if she asks. You can even let her go on thinking that the girl is an old flame of mine, if you like. That *is* what you told her, isn't it?'

'Yes,' Verity admitted. 'But I don't think I want her to go on thinking that.'

Sebastian stopped and turned her to him. 'Good.' He ran his lips in light kisses along her throat, sending her pulses racing. 'Tell her the truth then, but tell her the girl has gone away.'

'And has she?'

'I neither know nor care,' Sebastian said thickly as he took her in his arms yet again.

And neither did Verity as she lifted her lips to meet his and let herself drown in the strength of his embrace.

# CHAPTER FIVE

SEBASTIAN drove Verity and Paula to the station in Melford at eight-thirty the following Monday morning. The day was damp and misty and the roads busy with traffic. The train, too, was crowded with commuters, but Sebastian had reserved seats for them in a first-class carriage. He saw them into it, then took a parcel from his briefcase which he put into Verity's hands. 'A present for you.' His eyes met hers briefly in a warm, intimate smile that was for her alone, but then he turned to Paula. 'And one for you.'

The guard's whistle blew and Sebastian quickly left the carriage and shut the door, standing on the platform to wave as the train pulled out. Verity managed to resist the temptation to stand at the window, but looked out of it until the station was out of sight, now almost wishing that she hadn't agreed to go up to London with Paula. Since that night when he'd kissed her there had been no opportunity for them to be alone. Sebastian had been invited to spend the weekend with a friend, a long-standing engagement that he couldn't break. He had left on Friday afternoon and not returned until Sunday night, and now they were going away for two days. To Verity the days gone by and the two ahead seemed endless; she wanted to see him, be with him, talk to him— and, of course, be held in his arms and kissed again. Her pulses started to race every time she thought of those kisses out in the moonlit garden. She remembered the hard strength of Sebastian's body against hers, the possessiveness of his mouth.

'Aren't you going to open your present?'

Paula's voice was an unwelcome intrusion into her thoughts, but she smiled and said, 'Yes, of course. What was in yours?'

'The latest Laura Ashley book on design.' Paula held it out for Verity to see. 'Wasn't that thoughtful of him?'

'Yes. Oh!' Verity had unwrapped her parcel and found inside a beautiful woollen shawl, almost identical to the one she had lost in the river, but of a far better quality. 'Good heavens, I wonder how he managed to match it so well.'

'He evidently went to quite some trouble.' Paula leaned forward to look.

'I'm surprised that he even knew the colour when the shawl's stuck in the sluice and soaking wet.'

'It isn't there now—in the sluice, I mean. I took a walk up that way yesterday and remember noticing that it had disappeared.'

'Washed away, do you mean?' Verity asked.

Paula smiled. 'That's possible, of course, but if Sebastian managed to match it so exactly then I rather think he must have climbed down and fished it out, don't you?'

Verity sat back in her seat, looking at the shawl with deep pleasure. 'Yes, I suppose he must have done,' she agreed, and then shivered as she remembered the dangerous teeth of the sluice. 'He shouldn't have done it.'

But Paula misunderstood. 'Well, as he was responsible for your losing the old one, I don't see why he shouldn't replace it.'

'This is much better than mine; it's cashmere,' Verity murmured, holding the softness of the shawl against her cheek. 'It must have cost the earth.'

'Well, I shouldn't worry, Sebastian can afford it.'

'How do you know?' Verity demanded.

Paula laughed. 'I knew that would get to you. I asked Maggie, of course. She said that Sebastian is a partner in a development company.'

'And is it successful?'

'It would appear so. Maggie let fall that they've undertaken some fairly large projects in the past and have even bigger ones on the drawing-board.'

'So that's why he doesn't draw a salary from the estate.'

'And it also explains why he's always going away on business.' Paula gave Verity a speculative look. 'Does accepting that present mean that you're not mad at Sebastian any longer?'

'I wasn't mad at him,' Verity protested.

'Yes, you were; at least, you were certainly off him because of that girl.'

'As a matter of fact he explained all about her,' Verity said airily.

'He did?' It was Paula's turn to be intrigued. 'Well, what did he say?'

Verity teased her for a few minutes until Paula threatened to throw her book at her, and then Verity capitulated and said, 'It seems that she wasn't an old flame of Sebastian's, after all. He said that she worked at Layton House years ago and—and that's how she knew him,' Verity finished, remembering in time not to say anything about the girl being a troublemaker.

'But you said she called him "sweetie",' Paula was quick to remind her.

'So she did; but maybe she calls everyone that.'

'Well, I'm glad. I never really thought Sebastian was the type to go for that kind of girl,' Paula said with some satisfaction.

They both fell silent, but Verity couldn't help wondering if Paula, too, found Sebastian attractive. Not that it mattered, because *she* had been the girl that he had kissed, and she was sure that it was just the beginning; as soon as she got back to Layton House Sebastian would ask her for a date so that they could really be alone again.

The two days in London went by almost as quickly as Verity could wish. They did a little shopping before Paula went off to have lunch with her ex-boss, Piers Fielding, and Verity went to her house, then they met up again for another couple of hours in the West End before having a meal and taking in a film. Paula slept in late the next morning while Verity quietly cleaned the house and went through her mail, but by noon they were going round the baby and maternity departments in several big stores and spending a small fortune on clothes for Paula and fittings for the nursery.

'Are you sure you can afford all this?' Verity demurred.

'Quite sure,' Paula said with a laugh. 'Don't worry, it's my money, not part of the estate's.'

Paula always had liked shopping, for other people as much as herself, and she was in her element choosing clothes, and things for the baby. Her eyes sparkled and she was happy again, able to use her excellent taste and not having to worry about lack of money. She was born to be pampered like this, Verity thought, as she watched her friend try on a beautiful evening maternity dress. She was glad that Paula was recovering from her grief, but also felt a little sad; Paula looked so lovely in the dress that she knew it wouldn't be long before men began to interest her again and she would eventually choose one to marry. It wasn't that Paula was mercenary, and anyway she had inherited enough money from Simon to be independent if she chose, it was rather that she needed the security and admiration that only a man could give her, and would, practically, choose the most suitable candidate.

And what about me? Verity asked herself. Don't I need that, too? Yes, but only from one particular man, a man I would want to go on loving however little he had. And if I lost him I wouldn't even want to look at anyone else for a long, long time. Immediately following on that thought a picture of Sebastian came into her mind and brought her up short. Was he to be the man in her life? she wondered, her heart quickening. That he intrigued her was undeniable, and she was certainly attracted to him. But love? So soon? Verity pushed the thought to the back of her mind, knowing that she would think about it again when she was alone, when she had time, and instead gave all her attention to Paula as she was asked her opinion of the dress.

They left London at four-thirty before the worst of the rush hour, and Sebastian was waiting on the platform as they pulled into Melford Station a couple of hours later. 'I had an idea you might have a few parcels with you,' he said with a grin as he saw their shopping piled up on the seats.

'This is nothing,' Verity told him. 'You wait and see what Paula's having delivered.'

He took her hand to help her out and held it for a moment as he smiled at her. Verity wanted to go to him and kiss him, to show how much she'd missed him, but it was too soon for that. She could only return his smile and hope that her eyes said all she wanted to say.

Maggie had gone out to play bridge when they got back to the house. The girls went up to their rooms to change and unpack some of their parcels, and when they came down Sebastian was waiting in the drawing-room, ready to pour them pre-dinner drinks. 'I take it you had a good couple of days,' he said, as he handed them each a sherry.

'Well, I certainly did,' Paula admitted. She smiled at Sebastian. 'But it's nice to be back here.'

'Really? I'm pleased to hear it. And how about you, Verity?'

'Oh, I managed to buy a few things, too.'

His lips twitched. 'No, I meant, are you glad to be back, too?'

'Oh, I see.' She flushed a little and raised her eyes to meet his. 'Yes,' she said softly, 'I'm glad to be back.'

Their eyes held for a second, and then Sebastian turned to talk to Paula, but after about ten minutes he stood up. 'Mrs Chivers has left dinner all ready for us. If you'll go into the dining-room I'll bring it in.'

Verity got quickly to her feet. 'It's OK, I'll do it.'

'Certainly not,' Sebastian answered firmly. 'You must both be tired after all that shopping. I'll be two minutes.'

He was as good as his word, wheeling the hostess-trolley into the dining-room and insisting on serving them himself.

'Mmm, mushrooms,' Paula drooled when they reached the main course. 'They're the only thing I've really craved since I've been pregnant.'

'I'm afraid Mrs Chivers hasn't done very many; she must have remembered that Verity doesn't like them.' Sebastian served them out, giving Paula most of the dish and only taking a small helping for himself. 'As you're eating for two,' he grinned.

The food was delicious, better than Mrs Chivers' usual standard, and Sebastian opened a bottle of wine, which only he and Verity drank, Paula reluctantly sticking to water. After dinner Verity stacked the dishes in the dishwasher and made coffee before going to join the others in the sitting-room. Paula was sitting on the settee with Sebastian beside her as she told him about their trip and showed him a sample of the wall-paper she had finally decided on. They looked comfortable and at ease with one another, Verity thought, as she poured the coffee. A stab of emotion ran through her, so sharp that she spilt the coffee. But it wasn't jealousy, it was something far deeper than that.

'Here, let me help you.' Sebastian had seen and came to take the pot from her.

'Thanks. I must be getting clumsy.'

His eyes flicked to her and he gave her a small wink—and suddenly Verity knew quite definitely how she felt about him. It left her breathless and silent for quite some time, content to listen to Paula chatting away, and only making the effort to speak when she was asked a question.

After a couple of hours Verity began to think that Paula would never go to bed, but eventually the other girl's voice slowed and she got up from the settee, rather clumsily for Paula.

'Are you OK? Would you like me to come up with you?' Verity offered.

'Of course not. I'm fine.' She said goodnight and left them alone at last.

Verity, her eyes fastened on her hands in her lap, listened to Paula's footsteps going rather slowly up the stairs. She felt suddenly shy, like a teenager all over again.

Sebastian watched her, an amused look in his eyes, but then he said softly, 'Come here.'

Her eyes flew to his, her chin immediately coming up in defiance of such an autocratic order, but then she saw the desire darkening his face and the next moment she had gone to him and he was pulling her down on his lap.

'I missed you,' he told her forcefully, his mouth against hers as he ravaged it with small, insidious kisses. 'Ever since that last time I've wanted to kiss you again.'

Her arms went round his neck and Verity leaned against him, returning his embrace avidly, over-powered by his vehemence.

But all too soon Sebastian lifted his head, his face taut. 'Let's take a walk.'

But Verity nestled against him. 'It's cold outside.'

He smiled, but, putting his hands round her waist, lifted her to her feet. 'My mother will be home soon,' he reminded her.

So they got their coats and went out into the misty darkness. They stood for a few moments, tasting the cold air in their lungs, feeling the dampness of the night clinging to them. Verity pulled her coat closer at the neck and shivered a little, but then Sebastian put his arm round her waist and held her close against his side and her heart filled with eager anticipation.

'I know where we can go.' Walking quickly, he led her across the lawn to the rose garden, where there was a little wooden arbour covered in climbing roses built in the shelter of the wall, a place that lay in heavy shadow and still smelled of the faint musk of faded flowers. They sat close together to shut out the cold, and Sebastian put his hand on her neck, stroking her chin with his thumb, looking into her face before he bent to touch his lips to hers, softly at first, but then with a growing need that seared her senses. For several minutes there was no time for words, but then Sebastian sighed. 'I wish it were summer,' he murmured as he kissed her throat.

'Do you? Why?'

'Because then you wouldn't have so many clothes on.' His hands fumbled with the belt of her coat and then moved inside.

Verity caught her breath, and said unsteadily, 'I wish it were summer, too, then your hands wouldn't be so cold.'

He laughed, and pulled her to him to kiss her deeply, exploring her mouth like a man who had all the time in the world. A quiver of awareness ran through Verity as she leaned against his arm, her mouth open under his, her senses drowning in a long spiral of pleasure and growing excitement. His hand moved up from her waist, found the soft lace of her bra and moved it aside as he began to caress her. His fingers, firm yet gentle, and oh, so knowledgeable, created ripples of desire that spread into waves of heat that made her gasp and move voluptuously under his hand.

Her reaction could only increase Sebastian's own hunger, and his mouth grew more demanding as his arm tightened and he held her close against him. And then his mouth left hers as he kissed her eyes, the line of her cheek, her neck. His voice thickening, he murmured her name against the soft skin of her throat, and now his hands were hot, burning hot, as he fondled her. Verity moaned, her body hardening and arching towards him, her senses on fire and a great longing rising deep inside her. She put her hands on either side of his head and could feel the damp sweat of perspiration on his skin as he kissed her again.

Verity had lost all sense of time and place, and it was Sebastian who eventually drew back. He put up an unsteady hand to push a lock of hair back from his forehead. 'Phew! It certainly feels like summer now; I'm burning up.' He shot his wrist forward to try to see his watch, but it was too dark. 'I wonder what the time is? Mother should have been home by now.'

'Perhaps she is home,' Verity suggested.

'I didn't see any car lights. Did you?'

'No, but then I wasn't exactly looking out for them.'

Sebastian laughed softly and nuzzled her ear. 'No, I have to admit that I had other things on my mind, too.' But he frowned and drew back. 'I think we'd better go in and check.'

They began to walk back to the house, but Verity teased him on the way back, putting her arms round his waist and nibbling at his ear, so that they stopped more than once as Sebastian, goaded, grabbed her and soundly kissed her. It was only as they came round to the front of the house that Verity noticed that the light was on in Paula's room. 'I hope she's all right!' she exclaimed in concern.

'Probably reading in bed.'

But their footsteps quickened as they hurried to the door. It was on the latch and Verity pushed it open, filled with a sudden sense of alarm and urgency.

Paula's screams filled their ears as soon as they entered the hall. She was on the floor on the landing at the top of the stairs, half lying against the wall, slumped against it and with her arms across her stomach as she cried out in agony.

'Paula!' Verity flew up the stairs and threw herself down beside the other girl. 'Oh, darling, what is it? Is it the baby?'

'Help me! Help me!' Her eyes wild, Paula clutched at Verity and then cried out again as another spasm of pain shot through her.

Below them, Verity heard Sebastian talking on the phone, and then he came bounding up the stairs. 'I've called an ambulance. Has she told you what's the matter?'

'No. But feel her head, she's so hot. And she's in such pain.'

Suddenly Paula made terrible choking noises, and Sebastian quickly picked her up and carried her into the bathroom where she was terribly sick, heaving her heart up.

'What is it? What's the matter with her?' There was real terror in Verity's voice as she tried to help.

'I don't know. Look, she's shivering now. Get a blanket to put round her.' Verity yanked one off the bed and Sebastian gently lifted Paula and wrapped her in it, then laid her on the bed. She was still groaning, but didn't seem to be quite so bad now. 'Will you look after her for a few minutes while I go and put the floodlights on to guide the ambulance?'

'Yes, of course.' Verity put her arms round Paula and tenderly stroked the hair that was clinging to her damp head. 'Oh, Paula, what is it? What is it?'

Perhaps the intensity of her words got through, because Paula opened her eyes and gave a long, whimpering moan. 'Where were you? I couldn't find you.' Tears poured down her cheeks. 'Oh, Verity, I feel so ill.'

'You'll be all right. An ambulance is coming. You'll soon be fine.' Verity spoke as reassuringly as she could, but she was scared to death, fear for her friend gripping her heart. She rocked her in her arms like a child and made soothing noises, but Paula suddenly began to scream again, throwing herself around on the bed in agony.

Sebastian came running in and caught hold of Paula, preventing her from falling off the bed and hurting herself. He thrust a radiophone and a small book into Verity's hands. 'This is Mother's address book. I think she's playing at the Naughtons' tonight. See if you can get hold of her, will you?'

Her hands shaking, Verity managed to look up the number, but when she went to use the phone found that it was already switched on. 'It's already on. I——' She broke off, her mind in a whirl, and hurriedly punched the numbers, waiting impatiently for it to ring. 'Pléase, is Maggie there? Yes? No, just tell her to please come home at once. Paula is ill. Yes, we've sent for an ambulance. Yes. Thank you.'

She threw the phone aside as it became evident that Paula was going to be ill again. Sebastian carried her into the bathroom and Verity held her as she retched horribly with nothing left in her stomach. Afterwards Verity gently washed her face, and then glanced up to see Sebastian leaning against the wall, beads of sweat glistening on his face. But he quickly straightened up and said, 'The ambulance should be here any minute. I'll take her downstairs.'

Lifting Paula, he carried her out on to the landing, but seemed to stagger a little. Catching his arm to steady him, Verity said anxiously, 'Are you all right? Is she too heavy for you?'

'No, of course not. I'm fine.' He tightened his hold and went down the stairs carefully, reaching the hall just as the flashing blue light of the ambulance filled the open doorway.

The ambulancemen were marvellously efficient and had Paula inside the vehicle within seconds.

'You go with her,' Sebastian said, helping Verity inside. 'I'll wait for Mother and follow you in the car.'

The nearest hospital was at Melford and at that time of night the roads were almost deserted, but it still seemed like light years before they reached it and Paula was rushed into the casualty department. Verity stood alone, waiting, biting her thumb in nervous dread.

A sister came hurrying towards her. 'You came with Mrs Layton, didn't you?' And when Verity nodded, 'Have you been with her all evening? Do you know what she's eaten?'

'Eaten?' Verity stared, then pulled herself together. 'We were in London, we had lunch in a restaurant. But we both had salad.'

'And this evening?' the nurse prompted. 'Do you know what she had for dinner?'

'Why, yes, we all had the same.'

'You're sure? You ate exactly the same food as Mrs Layton?'

'Yes. Oh—except for the mushrooms, of course.'

The nurse put her hand on Verity's arm. 'Are you saying that Mrs Layton had mushrooms but you didn't?'

'Yes. But Sebastian had some.'

'And is he all right?'

'Why, yes, I——' She broke off, her mind suddenly picturing Sebastian leaning against the wall, and her voice became uncertain. 'I think he is. Why? Do you think Paula has food poisoning?' she asked anxiously.

'It could be very likely. I'll go and tell the doctor.'

She hurried off and Verity sat down on a chair, not knowing if this was good news or bad. She had been so afraid that Paula might be having a miscarriage or have appendicitis or something; compared to them food poisoning seemed almost mild. But then she remembered Paula's agonised screams and her mind filled with worry again.

It was almost twenty minutes later before Maggie and Sebastian arrived at the hospital. Verity jumped to her feet and ran to meet them, her eyes going swiftly to Sebastian's face. He was hiding it well, but one look was enough to confirm her fears; his features were drawn in tightly as he fought to conceal the pain, but there were tell-tale beads of moisture on his lip and his forehead.

'What's the matter with Paula? Do they know? Have they said anything to you yet?' Maggie asked at once.

'Nothing definite. But they asked me what we had for dinner. They—they said it could be food poisoning.' She turned to Sebastian. 'But the only thing I didn't have that Paula did was the mushrooms at dinner. But you had those. Are you feeling OK?'

Maggie's eyes widened in horror. She looked at Sebastian sharply and then said, 'He certainly isn't. Call a nurse, Verity.'

'I'm all right,' Sebastian began to protest, but was given no chance to go on. Within minutes he, too, had been whisked away by the efficient nurses.

'Sebastian told me what happened, but perhaps you could tell me again,' Maggie said as they sat down. Verity did so, and Maggie shook her head in disbelief. 'I just can't understand it. How could shop-bought mushrooms possibly have made them ill? Unless...' She fell silent for a moment, a worried frown on her face, then said, 'I tried to phone the house twice this evening to speak to Sebastian, but I couldn't get through. Were you using the phone a lot?'

'No, no one made any calls—except when Sebastian rang for the ambulance, of course.'

'No, it would have been before then. How strange.'

'Do you—do you think Paula will be all right?' Verity asked, wanting to have the dread in her mind comforted away.

Reaching over, Maggie took hold of her hand and patted it. 'I'm sure she will. And I'm sure the doctors are all very experienced and will do their best for her. But as I didn't see her...' She shook her head. 'I'm sure *Paula* will be all right.'

The slight emphasis made Verity's eyes widen. 'Surely you don't think she could lose the baby? But she's six months; if the baby started to come because of this it would still be OK, wouldn't it? It would still live?'

Maggie looked at her for a moment, her eyes troubled. 'We must certainly hope and pray so. If only I'd been there,' she added with a vexed sigh.

Verity turned away, feeling sick inside. She hadn't been there either, when Paula had needed her. The pregnant woman had been left alone in the house while she and Sebastian had been indulging in a spot of lovemaking, in the beginnings of—of what? An affair? Verity buried that thought, unable to think of anything but her own guilt. She should never have left Paula alone; hadn't she expressly come here to look after her friend until the baby was born?

The two women sat for what seemed an eternity, not talking much, Maggie apparently busy with her own thoughts and Verity racked by her conscience.

It was Sebastian who came out first. His face was very pale, his cheeks drawn, but apart from that he seemed perfectly all right. Hope flared in Verity's heart and she went quickly to him. 'Is there any news of Paula?'

'I asked, but they're still working on her, evidently.' Then he quickly put out his hand and caught her arm. 'But I'm sure she'll be all right. I'm over it now.'

'Yes, but you gave Paula most of the mushrooms and you're not pregnant!' Verity said in a sudden burst of anger.

He gave a harsh, mirthless laugh. 'It's hardly likely that I would be.'

Maggie had come up to them and said, 'Are you really all right, Sebastian? You look dreadfully pale. You haven't dismissed yourself against their orders or anything, have you?'

'I'm fine,' he answered in a tone that warned her not to fuss. 'There's a coffee machine over there; I'll get you some.'

He walked away and Maggie looked after him worriedly. 'I really think he ought to go home and go to bed; he doesn't look at all well.'

Belatedly, Verity realised that she hadn't even asked Sebastian how he was. But she was so worried about Paula, and he had seemed hardly ill at all in comparison. She watched him at the coffee machine and saw him put a hand against it as if to support himself. She took an instinctive step to go to him, but Maggie caught her arm and said, 'Here's the doctor.'

Verity turned quickly, her eyes searching the doctor's face. 'Mrs Layton? How is she?'

His face was grave and Verity's heart sank, but he said, 'We have every hope that she will make a full recovery. But she has been very ill.'

'And the baby?'

He gave an expressive shrug. 'At the moment she still has it and we've managed to sedate her, but it's still possible that the stomach cramps she's gone through might bring on a premature labour.'

'When will you know whether it will be all right?' It was Maggie who asked the question that Verity couldn't bring herself to voice.

'We want to keep her here for at least a week; if she doesn't give birth in that time then there's every chance of her keeping the baby for the natural period.'

'Can I see her?' Verity asked anxiously.

'I don't really think there's much point. She's asleep, and it will be much better if you go home and come back tomorrow.' The doctor glanced at Sebastian who had come up behind them, and his voice hardened. 'And *you* should definitely be in bed, preferably in a ward here where I can keep an eye on you.'

But Sebastian merely said, 'What time tomorrow can we visit Mrs Layton?'

'Any time. I've followed your instructions and put her in a private room.'

The doctor nodded and turned away, but had only gone a few yards when Verity ran after him and caught his sleeve. 'Just a moment. Please.' He stopped, looking at her enquiringly, and she said earnestly, 'Paula—Mrs Layton, she's a widow. Her husband was killed a few months ago. The baby is all she has now. You will do your best to help her keep it, won't you?'

'We always do our best,' he said wryly. But then he patted her shoulder. 'Don't worry, we'll take good care of her.'

He went through the doors leading into the ward and Verity turned back to where the others were waiting for her. Maggie was talking heatedly, and as Verity came up she heard her say, 'But how could cultivated mushrooms possibly give you food poisoning? Mrs Chivers would surely have realised if——' She saw Verity and broke off abruptly. 'Let's go home; you both look terrible.'

'I want to stay,' Verity began. 'She might wake up in the night and need someone.'

But Sebastian said forcefully, 'No, you're going home. All Paula needs now is sleep.' And, taking her arm, he led her firmly towards the main door. Verity resisted him for a moment, but suddenly found that she couldn't defy the authority in his voice and let him take her outside.

Maggie insisted on driving, and neither Verity nor Sebastian argued. Verity sat in the back, her eyes closed, her head against the upholstery. She felt terribly tired, as if all her strength had been drained out of her, but the guilt and the worry were still there, hardly alleviated at all by the doctor's reassurance.

When they reached the house Maggie insisted on seeing her up to her room so there was no opportunity to be alone with Sebastian, and somehow she didn't want to apologise to him in front of his mother. And he looked quite ill now, spent and exhausted. Dimly it came to Verity that it must have taken a great deal of strength and determination for Sebastian to have taken care of Paula as he had without saying a word about his own illness. They owed him a great deal, but now wasn't the time to tell him that, either.

She didn't sleep that night, just lay in bed, mentally praying for her friend, and by six o'clock she couldn't stand it any longer and went downstairs in her nightdress to phone the hospital. They merely told her that there was no change, which in itself was good news, she supposed, although it didn't do much to alleviate her anxiety.

'How is she?' Sebastian was coming down the stairs, a robe pulled loosely over his pyjamas, or at least over his pyjama trousers—his chest was obviously bare.

Even then, when her mind was full of anxiety, Verity felt a stirring of awareness as she saw the smoothness of his skin. She wanted to go to him, touch him, run her hands over the rippling hardness of his chest. To be held and caressed as he had caressed her last night.

*Last night when she should have been with Paula!*
The thought hit her like a blow and brought a sense
of shame that made her say shortly, 'She's still the
same.'

He came across the hall to put a comforting arm
round her, but Verity moved away, her head down,
not looking at him. Sebastian gave her an assessing
glance. 'Is something troubling you, Verity?'

'Paula's been terribly ill. She could have died! She
still might lose the baby. Isn't that trouble enough?'
she burst out on an anguished note.

'Yes, of course. But is it any reason to shut me
out?'

She bit her lip. 'I'm sorry, I haven't asked you how
you feel.'

'Thank you, I'm perfectly well again now.'

'And yesterday; I'm afraid I didn't thank you for
helping Paula the way you did when you were feeling
terrible yourself,' she said in a small, formal tone.

His voice rough, he said, 'You don't have to thank
me and you know it. Damn it, Verity, what is it?'

'Don't you dare swear at me!' she retorted, her voice
rising.

She went to go past him to reach the stairs, but he
caught her wrist and swung her round. 'Tell me!'

For a moment she fought him, beating her fist
against his chest, but then Sebastian put his arms
round her in a bear-hug, imprisoning her against him.
Verity felt the hardness of his body through the thin
material of their nightclothes and a great wave of sen-
suousness filled her, and with it a need to be comforted and have everything put right. She gave a great
sob and burst into tears.

'Verity, sweetheart.' His lips chased a tear down her cheek and kissed it away. 'What is it?'

'I should have been here last night! I wasn't here when Paula was ill and needed me.'

'Oh, I see.' Verity glanced up, and through her tears surprised a look of relief in Sebastian's face. 'But that's nonsense, really it is. How could you possibly have known that——?'

'Oh, no! Have you heard from the hospital? Has something dreadful happened to Paula?' Maggie came running down the stairs towards them, her dressing-gown held round her and a look of fear on her face.

'No, it's all right,' Sebastian assured her quickly. 'Things just got a bit much for Verity, that's all. The hospital said that Paula's still OK.'

'Oh, thank goodness! For a terrible moment...' Maggie visibly pulled herself together and looked at them with relief, her eyes widening a little when she saw how closely her son was holding their guest. 'I think we could all do with a cup of tea,' she said briskly. 'Last night was one of the worst I've ever known. Verity, my dear, perhaps you ought to put something more on; we don't want you going down with a cold,' she said tactfully as she walked towards the kitchen.

'Oh, yes, of course.' Verity extracted herself from Sebastian's arms, conscious now of how the silk material must cling to her figure. She lifted a finger to wipe away the tears and ran upstairs. At the top she turned to go to her room and glanced down. Sebastian was standing where she had left him, watching her, with such a look of flaring desire in his eyes that she gasped aloud in recognition. She stood there for a long moment, their glances locked, so totally on the same wavelength that she could almost feel the heat of his need for her. But then she gave a little cry and tore herself away from that smouldering gaze to run to her room.

She didn't go down again, instead throwing herself back into bed and pulling the covers up around her neck, feeling quite unable to face Sebastian. Maggie brought the cup of tea up to her and stayed to chat, her words so reassuring that it was soon evident that Sebastian must have told her about Verity's guilt feelings. 'We can none of us blame ourselves,' she said soothingly. 'It was pure chance that you were the one who didn't like mushrooms, or you would have been ill, too. But Paula is going to need you now, to help pass the time away while she's in hospital, and to reassure her when she worries about the baby.'

Verity nodded, glad that there was something useful she could do, but said, 'I just don't understand how the mushrooms could have made her so ill.'

'No, nor do I,' Maggie agreed, a frown of deep anxiety in her eyes. 'But we don't know for sure it was that; it might have been something else.'

Maggie left soon afterwards, and Verity got dressed and drove to Melford, impatiently waiting for the florist's to open so that she could buy a basket of flowers to take into Paula. She spent nearly the whole day at the hospital, holding Paula's hand, talking to her, anxiously looking for any signs of improvement in the pale, weak figure, and often being rewarded with a smile that gave her great encouragement. Sebastian looked in in the afternoon, bringing with him a huge bouquet of golden chrysanthemums, but Paula was asleep and didn't see him. He beckoned

Verity outside into the corridor and she went reluctantly, afraid to leave Paula in case she woke.

'I won't keep you more than a moment. I just wanted to tell you that a health inspector came to see me this morning; evidently all cases of food poisoning have to be reported. He said that there must have been toadstools mixed up with the mushrooms. Just a few, not very many, not enough to kill us or anything, but quite enough to have made Paula and me ill.'

Her eyes widening in horror, Verity said, 'But how could toadstools have got mixed up with ordinary mushrooms? Surely the shop where they were bought would have——?'

'They weren't bought in a shop,' Sebastian interrupted. 'Mother spoke to Mrs Chivers this morning and it seems that the mushrooms Mother had bought were used up earlier, but as Mrs Chivers knew that Paula has such a great fancy for them she bought some off Old Taffy.'

'Who on earth is that?'

'He's a very old man who lives in the village. To earn some money he goes out early in the mornings to pick mushrooms, and he sells them and stuff that he grows in his garden to people in the village. We can only think that the poor old boy's eyes are going and that he mistook some toadstools for mushrooms.'

'But Mrs Chivers—surely she noticed the difference?'

Sebastian shook his head. 'She was brought up in a town; she's been buying mushrooms from Old Taffy for years and just naturally assumed that they were all right, the same as they've always been. She feels terrible about what's happened, of course.' He put his hands on Verity's arms. 'So, you see, in no way were you to blame.'

But she shook her head stubbornly. 'I should have been there.'

Sebastian looked as if he was going to protest, but some nurses came along, wheeling a patient, and he straightened up. 'We'll talk some other time. Mother and I will come back this evening to see Paula.' But before he let her go he pulled her to him and kissed her lightly on the cheek. Verity's eyes flew to his, her heart fluttering a little at this sign of possession, but then she drew quickly back. He gave a wry kind of grin, then lifted a hand in farewell before striding away.

Verity went back into Paula's room, and when Paula woke told her about the toadstools.

'I shall never eat another mushroom as long as I live,' Paula said with a great shudder. 'I really felt as if I was going to die. In fact, it was so painful I almost wanted to die.'

'Oh, Paula, don't, please. I was so afraid for you.'

Paula squeezed her hand. 'Sorry, didn't mean to give you a fright.' A bleak expression came into her face. 'We don't seem to have had much luck since we came to Layton House, do we? First you get knocked down and nearly killed, and now this.'

Verity lifted her head to stare at her. 'No,' she agreed hollowly. 'We don't, do we?'

# CHAPTER SIX

THE week that Paula was in the hospital passed terribly slowly at first. During the first couple of days she had several bouts of depression, but Verity was always there to comfort or talk her out of them, and luckily Paula's condition improved and she bounced back remarkably quickly as soon as she was sure she wasn't going to lose the baby. The day she came home they had a celebration dinner, but 'definitely no mushrooms', as Maggie said firmly.

Paula laughed ruefully. 'No, I shall have to find something else to crave.' She looked around at them and smiled. 'You've all been so kind to me, coming to visit me and sending the flowers; I really feel as if I'm part of the Layton family now.'

'Of course you are,' Maggie responded at once. 'Why, you were my stepson's wife, and that makes you the equivalent of a daughter-in-law, you know.' She looked at Verity and seemed about to say something, but then smiled and changed her mind.

Verity fussed around Paula for a couple more days, trying to make up for letting her down, until Paula turned round and firmly told her to stop behaving like a mother hen. 'I'm fine now, really. And it's time we got started on the nursery or it won't be ready when the baby arrives.'

Verity opened her mouth to protest, but recognised the stubborn lift to Paula's chin and shut it again, knowing that she would be wasting her time. 'OK, so let's get to work,' she said with a happy grin.

When Sebastian came home from his office late that afternoon he found the old nursery almost completely cleared of its contents and Verity whistling contentedly as she stripped off the old wallpaper. He stood in the doorway, leaning against the jamb, an amused smile on his lips as he watched her work. Bending to pull off a piece near the floor, Verity noticed him and straightened up. 'Hi.'

'Hello.' He strolled over to her and looked at the wall she was working on. 'How's it going?'

'Quite well, really, although there must be half a dozen layers of paper on the wall. Didn't decorators ever strip the paper off in the old days?'

'Evidently not. Didn't you know that old houses are held together by wallpaper inside and ivy outside?' he told her teasingly.

'Well, I hope the place doesn't fall apart when I get this lot off.'

'I wouldn't be surprised if you found some cracks.' He turned towards her. 'Where's Paula, isn't she supervising?'

'She was, but she's having a rest now.'

'And Mother's out, so that gives us a chance to have a talk, doesn't it?' Sebastian said firmly, his eyes regarding her steadily.

'Do we—do we need to have a talk?' Verity temporised, her heart immediately beginning to beat faster.

'Definitely. But first I think we need to do this.' And, drawing her to him, Sebastian took her in his arms and kissed her.

It had been a long time; not since that morning after Paula had been taken ill had they been together like this. That she could have gone to him for comfort, Verity knew, but she also knew that it wouldn't have stopped at comfort and she couldn't have coped with that complication when Paula was so ill. Even now she held back a little, almost afraid of this over-whelming sexual awareness she felt whenever he held her. And often when he didn't; there wasn't a day or night now when she didn't think of him and hunger for his touch.

Sebastian raised his head and she opened her eyes to find him watching her, his left eyebrow raised questioningly. 'I'm sorry,' she said in a hesitating tone. 'I haven't been very—very receptive lately, have I?'

'And you're still not.' He ran a finger lightly down her profile and stopped at her lips. 'Not completely. But now that Paula's better maybe we can rectify that.'

'How—how do you mean?' Verity murmured against his finger, turning each word into a kiss.

Sebastian smiled. 'By seeing more of each other, for a start.' He bent to bite her ear-lobe, his lips pulling gently, and let his hand move on down her chest to lightly brush her breast.

Just that feather touch was enough; Verity quivered and lifted her hands to his shoulders, her hips arching in involuntary desire. He dragged her to him then, his arms holding her pressed tightly against him in a sudden wave of hunger. His lips took hers fiercely, passionately, sending her mind reeling, her senses lost in a roaring tide of sensuality.

'Verity! Darling.' He kissed her eyes and her throat, raging kisses that made her give little moans of excitement. 'Come out with me tonight,' he said thickly.

'We'll have dinner and then we'll dance. Say yes, Verity.'

'What?' Verity put her hands against his chest and held him away from her, her senses whirling so much that she had hardly taken in what he said. 'What did you say?'

He laughed and, taking hold of her hands, kissed her palms. 'I merely asked you to have dinner with me tonight. There's a nightclub in Melford where you can eat and dance, and then we——'

'No!' Verity broke away from him. 'You know I can't leave Paula.'

He became still, his eyes on her agitated face, and then straightened up. 'You're forgetting that Mother will be here. I'm not asking you to leave her on her own.'

'I'm sorry, Sebastian, but that doesn't make any difference. Paula might need me.'

His face hardened. 'And what about your needs? Or mine, for that matter? It's been over a week since I've even been able to kiss you. How long are you going to go on playing nursemaid?'

Verity frowned. 'Just so long as she needs me, of course.'

'You're not Paula's servant,' Sebastian said harshly. 'Neither are you her wife.'

'Well, of course not!' Verity retorted indignantly. 'But I am her friend. I'm all she's got, Sebastian. I let her down terribly badly once because of——' she broke off abruptly '—and I'm not going to do it again,' she finished.

'Which brings us back to that talk we were going to have,' Sebastian said grimly. 'And I see now that you're not only blaming yourself, but me as well.'

'No, it isn't like that,' Verity protested. 'Of course I don't blame you. You were marvellous when you were so ill yourself. I don't know anyone else who could be so strong. I only wish that I had been as strong. But I wasn't; I wanted to go out into the garden with you and I—I hardly gave Paula a thought.'

'Well, I suppose that's something.' He gave her a brooding look. 'All right, I agree, maybe we shouldn't have left her, although how we were supposed to guess that... But if that's the case then I'm as much to blame as you, and we've both been taught a lesson. Neither of us would dream of leaving Paula alone now. But surely you realise that she'll be perfectly safe with my mother?'

Verity hesitated, shaking her head worriedly. Common sense told her that he was right, but somewhere deep in her heart she had this instinctive fear that something terrible might happen to Paula again if she wasn't there to look after her. 'I'm sorry, but I feel that I must be with her—just until the baby is born.'

'But that's three months! Are you seriously trying to tell me that you're going to act as Paula's shadow for all that time? You can't possibly mean that.'

Verity raised large, unhappy eyes to meet his. 'I'm sorry, I'm afraid I do.'

'And what about me?' he demanded, his voice rising in the anger of rejection.

'We'll be in the same house. We'll see each other all the time.'

'You mean when you have an odd half-hour to spare, when you're not running around behind Paula,' Sebastian said sneeringly.

Goaded, she turned on him angrily. 'Don't be so darn selfish! I came here to look after Paula until she has the baby, and that's what I'm going to do. You're just like every other man—you just want to be the centre of attention. Well, this time you definitely come second!'

They stood there, glaring at each other in the suddenly shattering silence. Then Sebastian, his voice glacial, said through gritted teeth, 'Well, thank you very much. At least I know where I stand.' And he turned on his heel and strode away, slamming the door behind him.

Verity slumped against the half-stripped wall, realising that she'd driven him away. Oh, no, she thought, and wondered whether to run after him and try and make it up, but at the same moment knew that he was too angry to listen. Then the door opened and she stared up with hope in her eyes, only to have it dashed when Paula came in.

'What was all that about?' the other girl demanded with avid curiosity.

'Oh, you heard.'

'Of course. It sounded as if you two were having a hell of a fight.'

'We were,' Verity said feelingly, but then remembered what it had been about and hastily added, 'Or rather, we were just having a difference of opinion.'

'What about?' Paula repeated insistently.

'Oh—er—politics,' Verity lied feebly.

'Politics?' Paula stared at her in disbelief. 'But surely Sebastian wouldn't get that heated over something like that? After all, he is civilised. You must have...' Her voice trailed off as she eyed Verity narrowly. 'Are you telling me to mind my own business?'

'I think that might be quite a good idea now that you mention it, yes.' Verity turned her back on Paula and began to vigorously jab at the wallpaper.

'Really? How interesting. You and Sebastian.' Paula gave a catlike grin that Verity found infuriating. 'So how long has this been going on?'

'There is *nothing* going on,' Verity said with precise emphasis.

Paula came to stand beside her. 'You're making holes in the wall,' she pointed out maddeningly. 'You know, you never did tell me where you'd got to on the night I was taken ill; you just said that you'd gone for a walk. Could it have been for a spot of moon-light canoodling with Sebastian, I wonder?' And when she saw the colour rush to Verity's cheeks she clapped her hands and said, 'I'm right! I knew it. Well, well, well. You old sly-boots. Why didn't you tell me?'

'There's nothing to tell,' Verity said crossly. Then, immediately contrite, said, 'Paula, I'm so terribly sorry—for that night. I shouldn't have gone. I should have stayed here with you. But it won't happen again, I can definitely promise you that,' she added fervently.

'Really? Sebastian might have something to say about that,' Paula said jokingly, but then saw Verity's eyes shadow and immediately jumped to all the right conclusions. 'Is that what you were rowing about just now? It was, wasn't it?' And when Verity nodded shamefacedly she said roundly, 'Then you're a fool, Verity. Don't you know that no woman should ever let anyone else come between her and the man she wants? And you do want Sebastian, don't you?'

But that was going too far, even for Paula. A closed look came into Verity's face and she turned away. 'I really don't have any feelings about him at all,' she said shortly.

Paula gave her back an amused, contemplative look. 'I think I'll wear my new evening dress this weekend,' she said musingly.

Verity swung round in surprise. 'Why, is it a special occasion?'

'Not yet, but it could be,' Paula said almost coquettishly.

'What do you mean?' Verity demanded, knowing her friend of old and immediately suspicious.

Paula merely smiled and made for the door, but turned as she reached it and said over her shoulder, 'Well, if you're not interested in Sebastian, maybe I'll make a play for him myself!'

'Paula!' But Verity was talking to a closed door. She stood there for a few moments, looking after Paula fumingly, but then turned to start work again and caught sight of herself in the mirror over the fireplace. Old jeans and baggy sweater, her hair tied back from her head with a piece of ribbon and bits of wallpaper stuck to her; she looked dreadful. Verity gave a howling groan of anger and threw the scraper at the wall in frustrated rage.

Paula wore one of her new maternity dresses to dinner that evening, and she had also gone to town with her make-up so that she looked very fragile and lovely. She shot Verity a wicked glance, and during dinner announced that she had booked a table at a restaurant for Saturday night and was taking them all out for a meal. 'Just as a small thank-you for all your kindness to me,' she told them.

'That will be lovely,' Maggie beamed. 'But you really don't have to, you know.'

'I want to,' Paula insisted. She looked at Sebastian laughingly. 'But I think having to escort three ladies will be rather too much for poor Sebastian, so, if you wouldn't mind, I'd like to invite Piers Fielding as well. He's my ex-boss,' she explained for Maggie's and Sebastian's benefit.

'Of course. Perhaps you'd like to invite him for the weekend?'

'If it wouldn't be too much trouble. And if he can make it, of course.'

Verity gave her a surprised, speculative look, wondering why she had chosen to invite Piers down. Paula caught her eye and immediately guessed her thoughts, but only gave her a teasing, 'wouldn't you like to know?' look and turned to talk to Sebastian. Paula was obviously in one of her maddening moods, Verity decided in annoyance, knowing that she wouldn't get her friend to tell her anything until she was good and ready. And she was in sparkling form too, drawing Sebastian out and making him laugh with her own anecdotes on life in Bahrain. Maggie, Verity noticed, was watching the two of them in amusement, but once or twice there was a contemplative look in her eyes. I wonder if she hopes the two of them will marry? The thought entered Verity's mind and made her feel suddenly cold. From Maggie's point of view it would be an ideal arrangement, of course; then there would be no fear of her losing this beautiful home, of having to change a life-style which she must love. And Sebastian? Wouldn't it be a perfect solution for him too? The cruel thought came into her mind and wouldn't go away. Then he would still have control of the estate and the use of all the money that went with it. And he would have Paula, who was lovely enough to make any man want her.

Her face set and tense, Verity shifted her gaze to Sebastian and saw that he was listening to Paula with laughter in his eyes. But, as if he felt her eyes on him, he half turned and glanced at Verity. His face changed, lost the laughter, grew withdrawn. Then he deliberately turned back to Paula, leaving Verity feeling as if she had been publicly spurned.

The evening wasn't a very pleasant one, with Paula at her most mischievous, Sebastian following her lead, and Maggie at a loss to know what it was all about. Verity was just glad when it was over. She spent the next day working alone in the nursery while Paula went into Melford with Maggie to register with a doctor and go back to the hospital for a check-up. At mid-morning Verity broke off for a mug of coffee, which she drank sitting on the deep window-seat of the nursery. It was another beautiful day, the early morning mists having evaporated away, leaving the garden a rich gold in the sunlight. Verity couldn't resist it. She remembered that she needed to buy a book of stamps and post some letters, so she quickly changed, put on a jacket and set off to walk to the village, taking the short cut through the grounds.

She hadn't walked to the village before; they had always driven there in the car because it was too far for Paula, but this morning she strode out, glad to exercise her legs instead of keeping pace with Paula's slower steps. Despite the cloud in her life where Sebastian was concerned, the sun made her feel good this morning. Young and vital and alive. She jumped up and caught at the branch of a tree, sending a shower of leaves falling, and gingerly picked up a handful of horse-chestnuts, which she dropped into the river, leaning over the rail of the bridge and feeling no fear now as she looked down at the sluice.

Whenever she had reached this point before, she had turned off on to the path through the woods that took one round the edge of the estate, but this time she kept on the track and a few hundred yards further along came to a cottage where she knew that Mr and Mrs Chivers lived. It was quite a small place, a typical gamekeeper's cottage, except that the garden was overgrown and had a high and strong fence round it. Today was the Chivers' day off, and there was no smoke coming from the chimney, but as Verity approached there was the sound of loud barking and a big Alsatian dog bounded up to the fence, jumping up against it and leaving Verity in no doubt as to why the fence was so strong.

Having lived most of her life at boarding-school and in a city, Verity wasn't very familiar with animals. She hesitated, wondering whether the dog could get out, but the gate was securely padlocked and she felt confident enough to go closer. The dog didn't like it, however; she was definitely on his territory, and he snarled ferociously. 'Hello,' she said to him placatingly, but this overture only made him bare his teeth and growl menacingly. 'Chump, I'm not going to hurt you. Lord, I'm glad we're on different sides of the fence.' Verity looked pityingly at the dog, thinking how wild he looked and wondering if he was kept shut up in that small garden all the time. She went quickly past, and pushed the thought of the poor animal out of her mind as she enjoyed the rest of her walk.

It was a pretty village, but very small, with just a general-stores-cum-post-office, one pub and the

church, to serve a hundred or so houses and the out-
lying farms. After buying her stamps and walking
from one end of it to the other, there was nothing to
do but to turn round and walk back to the house.

Sebastian had gone away on business that day and
didn't come back until Saturday morning. At first
Verity thought that it would be a relief from tension
to have him go away, but found instead that she missed
him more than ever. All three women went into
Melford quite early in the morning to have their hair
done at Maggie's hairdresser's, and when they got
back Sebastian's car was parked outside the house.
Verity immediately felt her heart leap in her chest, but
it was Paula who said eagerly, 'Oh, good, Sebastian's
home.'

He came into the hall to meet them as they entered
the house, and went first to his mother and kissed her
on the cheek. Then it was Paula's turn, but she laughingly gave him her lips instead of her cheek. Sebastian
grinned lazily down at her. 'You look very lovely
today.'

'Thank you, kind sir. You will be rewarded in
heaven for that compliment. I'm in dire need of them
at the moment.'

Then it was Verity's turn to be greeted. He turned
to her, his glance going swiftly, warily, to her face—
but what he saw there made his eyes widen in recognition. Going to him, Verity put an unsteady hand
on his shoulder, said huskily, 'Hello, Sebastian,' and
quickly kissed him on the cheek before he could react.

He put out a hand to catch her arm as she turned
immediately away, but remembered his mother and
Paula and reluctantly drew back, his eyes following
her.

Verity made a point of keeping out of his way until Piers Fielding arrived just before lunch, when they all met up again. She had met Piers before, of course, when Paula had worked for him before she was married, and had always liked him in a casual way. He was a bachelor—but not quite confirmed yet, as he told everyone—and had a great artistic sense without at all being able to create any work of art. So he devoted himself to the creation of beautiful rooms instead, and, as he had a sound business sense, was very successful, with showrooms in Paris and New York as well as London. Piers was quite a bit older than the girls, nearly forty, and pleasant-looking rather than handsome, generous to people he liked, and had an unexpected sense of humour, so that Verity tended to think of him in an avuncular way.

He came loaded down with presents: chocolates and flowers for the women, and a very good bottle of brandy which he told Sebastian he was going to share with him.

'Good heavens, Piers! All these gorgeous presents. Have you had a win on the horses or something?' Paula exclaimed, her arms full of flowers.

'Far better than that, my darling girl. And far less risky, too. I've got a contract to do a sultan's new palace,' he said exultantly.

'Not the one you were telling me about? How marvellous! Come and tell us all about it over lunch.'

Piers was an ideal guest, keeping them all amused during the meal and then going off with Paula for a walk round the garden that took up most of the afternoon. Sebastian had gone out to keep an appointment with an architect, and so Verity was left with nothing to do but work on the nursery. She had

got to the rubbing-down-paintwork stage, and chose
that afternoon to do the window that looked out over
the garden. From there she could see Piers and Paula
quite clearly most of the time as they wandered apparently aimlessly round the garden. It looked as if
Paula was doing most of the talking, and very earnestly, too, often stopping and gesturing with her arms
as if she was trying to convince Piers of something.

A puzzled frown on her face, Verity stopped work
to watch them, wondering what Paula was up to. Then
she shrugged and gave up, knowing that Paula would
eventually tell her. That was the advantage of knowing
someone really well—although Paula enjoyed having
little secrets, Verity knew that she wouldn't be able to
resist confiding in her before too long.

At five o'clock Verity remembered that Paula had
that new evening dress to wear, and decided she had
better put some work into making herself look as good
as possible if she was going to compete. That she could
compete she was quite confident; although she was
not fragile-looking like Paula, Verity's slim figure and
beautiful hair attracted just as much attention. And
tonight she wanted to look especially good.

They were to meet in the sitting-room for an aperitif
before leaving for the restaurant. The men and Maggie
were down first, and Verity gracefully allowed Paula
the privilege of being last down to show off the new
dress. She was wearing her own favourite, a flame-
red dress of velvet and silk that set her hair on fire,
hair that she had drawn back from her face in a mass
of curls. The dress had a bow on one shoulder, leaving
the other bare, and fitted to her hips where there was
another, much larger bow, and the skirt swirled out
to her knees. The dress had drawn appreciative eyes

before and she hoped it would tonight, or at least one pair of eyes.

Verity ran lightly down the stairs and paused for a second before pushing open the sitting-room door. Sebastian was at the drinks tray and had his back to her, but Maggie exclaimed, 'Verity, how stunning! What a beautiful dress.'

Verity thanked her smilingly and returned the compliment, watching Sebastian out of the corner of her eye, knowing he had heard. But Piers came up to her and said, 'I've a good mind to kidnap you for my sultan; you would go beautifully with a room I have in mind for him.'

'But I wouldn't want to be just an ornament for anyone,' she pointed out, only half-jokingly.

'No, and I'm very much afraid he wouldn't treat you as one for very long if all I've heard about him is true,' Piers said with an exaggerated wink.

'Like that, huh?'

'Yes, he has quite a reputation.'

Piers went on talking, but Verity was looking at Sebastian. He finished pouring the drinks and turned with them in his hands. He took a pace forward then stopped, his eyes riveted on her. His gaze stayed on her face for a moment, then travelled down to her feet and slowly back again. And during those few seconds she read first admiration, and then an intensifying awareness that grew into desire as his eyes darkened. But it wasn't lust that was in his eyes; this was no mental stripping from a lascivious male. Verity felt not degraded but coveted, not cheapened but openly found attractive. And the knowledge was like a warm glow to her heart.

'Sebastian?'

His mother's amused reminder brought him back to reality. Sebastian's eyes crinkled into a wry grin. 'Sorry, Verity quite took my breath away.' He gave out the drinks and said to Verity, 'Your usual vodka and tonic?'

'Please.'

She moved to the sideboard to take it from him. He put the glass into her hand, but didn't let go for a moment and she saw that there was a strange, almost self-mocking look in his grey eyes. But the desire was still there, of that she was sure. He was about to say something, but just then the door opened and Paula made her grand entrance. Sebastian's eyes went to her over Verity's head—and stayed there.

Black suited Paula. She looked very lovely in that dress of black lace, her hair taken to the back of her head in a style that increased her look of fragility. Like a delicate china doll that might break if it wasn't handled with loving care, Verity thought, as she turned round. But then she saw the mischief deep in Paula's eyes and her lips twitched. 'You look fantastic,' she said aloud and went to kiss Paula on the cheek, but in her ear whispered, 'The merry widow?'

'Of course,' Paula whispered back. 'The scarlet woman?'

'Not quite.' Verity drew back and their eyes met, full of silent laughter and understanding.

The others, especially Piers, were quick to add their own compliments, which Paula accepted with easy grace, but then she'd had plenty of practice.

'What an unworthy pair we are, Sebastian, to have the company of three such beautiful women,' Piers remarked gallantly.

'Nonsense, you both look gorgeous. Don't they?' Paula appealed. She slipped her hand through Piers' arm. 'It isn't like you to be so humble.'

He gave a shout of laughter. 'Hoist with my own compliment.'

Sebastian took a glass of Perrier water over to Paula and she deliberately looked up into his eyes as she took it from him. He smiled back, his eyes amused, willing to go along with her in this game she was playing. But he knows it's a game, Verity thought; he knows she isn't really flirting with him. But even as she thought the words, a tiny flicker of doubt touched at the edge of her mind; was that what she *wanted* to believe?

She pushed the thought aside determinedly, and they were a merry party as they arrived at the restaurant that Paula had chosen. There another surprise awaited them in the amiable form of James Gillis, a bridge-playing friend of Maggie's whom Paula had invited to even up the number. They had been given a round table, but Paula, in the mischievous mood she was in, arranged the seating to suit herself, putting Verity between Piers and James Gillis and herself between Piers and Sebastian. But Verity didn't mind—in fact, she almost welcomed it; she wanted to see how Sebastian would behave towards her this evening without any prompting on her own part. The food was good and the service efficient and unobtrusive, the conversation light and general, no two people pairing off into long discussions, shutting out the others. And the atmosphere in the restaurant was pleasant, too, with a small group who played softly enough not to intrude, but loudly enough for the few couples who took to the tiny floor to be able to dance.

By tacit consent they all stayed at the table until they reached the coffee stage, then James and Maggie got up to dance, the others watching them for several minutes before Paula said, 'I've an idea that the older generation know how to enjoy themselves better than we do.' She turned to Sebastian with a smile. 'Shall we try to emulate them?'

'By all means.' He stood up and followed Paula on to the floor, then put his arms round her, bending his head to listen to her as they danced slowly round. Whatever Paula was saying, Sebastian seemed to find it very interesting, Verity noted. His eyes were on her face as she spoke animatedly, often gesturing with her right hand. At one point she must have mentioned Verity, for they both looked in her direction. Sebastian's eyes lingered, but Paula said something else and he gave her his complete attention again.

Verity glanced at Piers and surprised a look of sharp concern on his face. 'Ought she to be dancing in her condition? Especially when she was so ill such a short time ago.'

'She's OK,' Verity assured him. 'She's having a last fling.'

He raised his eyebrows. 'Before the baby's born, you mean?' And when Verity nodded, 'Oh, I see. Well, we must make the evening memorable for her, then.' Lifting his arm, he called the waiter over and ordered a bottle of pink champagne, which was waiting when the others returned to the table.

'Champagne! How lovely! Oh, but I can't drink any,' Paula lamented.

'Just half a glass won't hurt you. What do you think, Maggie?' Piers asked. And when Maggie smilingly agreed with him, he poured the wine and raised his glass as he looked round at them. 'Ladies and gentlemen, I'd like to propose a toast to our very lovely hostess. To Paula—and to her baby. May all go well for them both, now and always.'

They all joined in, raising their glasses and drinking as Paula said laughingly, 'You're all very kind, but this dinner was for me to thank *you*.'

The band played a faster number for a while, but when the music slowed Piers asked Paula to dance, and Sebastian turned to Verity. 'Shall we?'

'Why not?' She spoke lightly enough, but inwardly she wasn't very happy. Somehow tonight wasn't going right. She had expected more from Sebastian, although she wasn't quite sure what. Some show of possessiveness, perhaps—an indication to the others that she was special to him. But so far he had behaved no differently to her than he had to Paula. He had been just as attentive to them both; even now when they were dancing he held her no closer than he had her friend. And, now she came to think of it, he had never given any sign of his feelings towards her in public; only when they had been alone, out in the garden, had he shown her that he found her attractive.

That thought made her feel uncertain and vulnerable, and she was afraid that he was still mad with her for refusing to go out with him. She stiffened a little and moved away from him. Sebastian looked down at her quizzically. 'You're very quiet tonight.'

'Am I?' she answered unhelpfully.

He brought their coupled hands over and brushed his fingers down her cheek. 'I don't have to tell you how lovely you look, do I?'

'Oh, but I think you do.'

His eyes searched her face and then he bent to say, 'You're very beautiful, Verity.' She didn't speak, just looked into his eyes, and he gave a crooked smile. 'But that isn't enough, is it?'

She shook her head. 'No.'

He drew her closer to him so that their bodies touched and she felt his lips brush her hair. 'This isn't the time or the place,' he said softly. 'Tonight is Paula's night.' Putting a finger under her chin, he tilted her head so that she looked at him. 'Will you leave her and come out with me one night?'

Verity hesitated, but then remembered Paula telling her not to be a fool, and nodded. 'Yes. OK.'

A gleam of triumph came into his eyes and he lifted her hand to kiss her fingers. 'Tomorrow?'

'Yes.'

A quiver of nervous excitement ran through her, so strong that Sebastian felt it. His hand tightened on her waist and she read the sharpness of desire in his face. 'Till tomorrow, then, my beautiful girl,' he said softly.

Holding her close to him, he danced on, and now there was no need for words. Tomorrow, Verity thought in eager anticipation, but for now she was content and gave herself up to the pleasure of being held in his arms.

She danced with Piers after that, and then with James before she danced with Sebastian again. To keep things on a lighter note, she said, 'What were you and Paula talking about earlier?'

'Oh, nothing very much,' Sebastian said evasively.

'It didn't look like nothing much. Paula certainly had a lot to say.'

'It was merely business.'

'I suppose that means that I ought to mind mine?' Verity said wryly.

He grinned. 'Why don't you ask Paula?'

'Because I know she won't tell me.'

'And you thought it might be easier to get it out of me,' Sebastian said, and tapped her on the nose with his finger. 'Nosy.'

'I know Paula's up to something. And usually it's better to be forearmed when she gets one of her ideas. They've got me into trouble before.' And she went on to describe some of the madcap things they'd got up to at school, making Sebastian laugh, making the time pass until tomorrow.

And it was the next afternoon when Paula finally told Verity what she had in mind. During the morning Paula had gone for another walk with Piers, down the track and through the wood this time, and then she had been shut away in the sitting-room with Sebastian and Piers while Verity had helped Maggie to prepare lunch. This had proved to be a prolonged meal, and Piers had left immediately after it. After they had waved him off, Sebastian looked at Verity and said, 'I have to go and mark out some trees for felling; care to come with me?'

But Paula caught Verity's arm. 'No, you remember I said I wanted to talk to Verity.' She smiled at Sebastian. 'You can't have her until I've finished with her.'

Which was rather an unfortunate choice of words, all things considered. Sebastian shot Verity a mocking look and strode away towards the garage.

'All right,' Verity said resignedly. 'So what are you up to?'

'Let's go for a walk and I'll tell you. That was such a huge lunch, if I sit down I shall go to sleep.'

They changed into walking shoes and coats and began to stroll down through the garden, almost automatically turning in the direction of the river. 'Well?' Verity demanded. 'Come on, tell me the worst.'

Paula laughed delightedly. 'What makes you think it's something bad?'

'Because I know you of old. When it's something you think I might not like you never tell me until I don't have any choice.'

'Well, this time I'm sure you're going to agree that it's a marvellous idea.' Paula turned to her eagerly. 'Verity, you know we said that this area could do with a really good interior designer? Well, I've decided to start a business here.'

Verity stood still and stared at her. 'But how can you? You're pregnant. And even when the baby's born you——' She broke off. 'Oh, no! I'm a computer programmer, not a designer. I couldn't possibly run a shop and I——'

'Yes, you could,' Paula said eagerly. 'I'd do all the actual designing, but you would do all the management and administration side. You'd be marvellous at it. We'd make a great team, you know.'

'No, I don't know, and I don't think I want to. Paula, it's a crazy idea. We don't have enough experience for something like that.'

'But Piers has promised to help us all he can, even to put some contacts our way. He sometimes has to turn work away because he's so busy.'

'You mean Piers has agreed to this? You're even more persuasive than I thought. Paula, if you want to get back into interior design why don't you go and work for Piers again as soon as the baby's old enough?'

'Because that would mean living in London, but I want Simon's child to be brought up here, in Simon's house.'

Verity was silent for a moment, then began to walk on again before she said, 'Have you really thought this through? It isn't an impulse thing, is it?'

'No. As a matter of fact, I was thinking on these lines even before Simon was killed. Being just a wife wasn't enough because Simon was so wrapped up in his own business. I needed an interest of my own, something to give me my own identity. Can you understand that?'

'Yes, but the circumstances are different now. You'll have the baby and you'll have this house to run. If you take on a business as well it might be too much for you, you might have a conflict of loyalties.'

'Not if I have an efficient partner I can trust.'

'Namely, me.'

'Of course. Oh, Verity, can't you see? It would be ideal for us. We'd be able to work together. Wouldn't that be great? I've already spoken to Sebastian and he——'

'You've done *what*? Without telling me first?'

'Yes, because I wanted to get it all worked out first, to prove to you that I was really serious.'

Verity stared at her. 'And what did he say?'

'Well, I knew that he intended to develop an area in the centre of Melford, and I asked him if he might have a shop that was suitable for us, and he said he did. That we could have first choice of premises.'

'Oh, I see,' Verity said hollowly. 'He didn't raise any—any arguments?'

'Some,' Paula admitted. 'More or less the same as you.' They had reached the bridge, but both of them were so engrossed that they didn't notice and kept on walking along the track towards the village. 'But I convinced him that it was what I wanted to do, and he said he would help in any way he could. So, if both Piers and Sebastian think it's a good idea, won't you at least think it over, Verity?'

'Surely a business like that, with a showroom, would cost quite a lot of money to get started?'

'Yes, but I have plenty of money now,' Paula pointed out happily.

'But if I was to become your partner, then I would want to pay half, and I just don't have that kind of money.'

'Oh, you and your stubborn pride.' They argued for a few moments until Paula said, 'Well, you could always sell your house and use that money.'

'But then I wouldn't have anywhere to live,' Verity protested.

'Of course you would! You'd go on living with me at Layton House.' She saw Verity open her mouth and said swiftly, 'I'll even charge you rent if that will make you happy.'

Verity laughed, and was about to say something, but a movement in the trees caught her eye. 'Isn't that Sebastian? I thought he was working over in the woods.'

'Where?' Paula turned to follow her pointing arm, then suddenly gave a cry of alarm. 'Verity, that dog!'

And now Verity saw it. The fierce Alsatian that she had seen in the Chivers' garden. He came bounding down the track towards them, horrifying in his strength and wild savageness, his mouth drawn back over sharp white fangs, ferocious snarls coming from his throat.

'Run!' Paula turned and began to stumble back the way they'd come.

'No, keep still!'

But it was too late, the beast swerved in his stride and leapt for Paula's running figure, his powerful body hitting her in the back and knocking her down, his teeth going for her throat.

# CHAPTER SEVEN

'No!' Verity ran across and struck at the Alsatian, trying to knock him away, but he turned on her, raking his teeth across her hand and drawing blood.

'Verity, help me!' Paula was sobbing in terror and struggling to get to her feet.

Desperately Verity again tried to push the dog away, but this only seemed to enrage him further. He leapt at her, tearing her coat, but she ignored him as she tried to help Paula up. But then the dog bit Verity's wrist, sinking his teeth deep, and she cried out in pain. The pain made her suddenly see red and she yelled at the dog, trying to fight him off and at the same time keep him away from Paula. 'Go to the cottage!' she cried out. 'Get help!'

But Paula either didn't understand or was too afraid to hear. She got to her feet and began to run back towards the house, but her moving figure acted like a magnet to the dog and he immediately went snarling after her. With a furious, helpless sob, Verity threw herself between them as Paula went down again, covering her friend's body with her own. The animal came snarling round her head and she instinctively put her hands up to protect her face, but then cried out as she felt the dog's teeth tearing at her skin.

It seemed as if the nightmare would never end, that she would just have to lie here while the dog went on biting her, but through his growling she suddenly heard the clear note of a whistle. The dog drew back, his body tense. The whistle came again, and suddenly the brute was gone.

Verity couldn't believe it at first, and lay where she was, her body over Paula's, then she slowly eased herself off and sat up, looking fearfully round. A wave of sickness came over her as she saw the blood on her hands. She felt dizzy and had to fight hard to stop herself from fainting, but Paula was still lying on the ground, moaning with terror, pressing herself against the earth as if she wanted it to swallow her.

'Paula, it's all right. It's gone.' Verity lifted a hand to push her hair from her eyes and left a trail of blood across her face. 'Come on, we must get up.' Somehow she managed to get to her knees and then to stand. 'Come on, I'll help you.' Putting her arm through Paula's, she managed to haul her to her feet and hold her crying, trembling body in her arms. 'Hush. It's over now. You're safe.' Verity looked desperately round, knowing that Paula was in no state to walk back to the house. Then she remembered the whistle she'd heard and looked up the track towards the cottage, expecting Chivers to come hurrying to their aid as soon as he'd shut the dog away.

But no one came and she screamed out, 'Help! Help!' and then, in utter fury, 'Damn you! *Come and help us!*'

Her cry echoed through the trees, leaving behind an empty silence and making Verity feel utterly alone and helpless. It was only then that she remembered that Mr and Mrs Chivers had gone away for the weekend. Despair gripped her, and she felt like bursting into tears herself, but resolutely pushed it aside and said, 'Paula, I have to go and get help.'

'No!' Paula grabbed hold of her in a panic. 'No, don't leave me. That dog might come back.'

'Then we'll have to walk back. Do you think you can make it?'

'I don't know. I don't know. Oh, Verity, this place!' Her voice rose in raw terror.

'Hush, now, we're going to be fine. We'll just take it slowly. Come on, you can do it.' With her arm supporting Paula, they began to make their way slowly back to the house, but the pain in Verity's hands was intense now and she could feel the blood running down her arm. Gritting her teeth, Verity pressed on, murmuring words of encouragement to Paula, but it seemed an age before they crossed the bridge and came out into the garden. The sun was down now, and the cold shadows of dusk were lying over the lawns. They paused to rest and Verity dimly made out the figure of a man right over on the other side of the grounds, just emerging from the woods. He called out to them and she recognised Sebastian's voice, but she had no strength to answer him.

They began to struggle on again, and she saw Sebastian break into a run and come racing towards them. For a moment Verity was reminded forcibly of the dog as it had leapt at them. She stopped, her body trembling, and waited until Sebastian came up.

'Good grief! What's happened to you?' He stared at them in horrified disbelief.

'Go and get a car,' Verity said stonily, her face set and strained.

'But the blood! Let me see. Dear lord, Verity, I——'

'Just go and get a car!' she repeated, her voice rising, her eyes wild.

Recognising the hysterical note, Sebastian said quickly, 'All right. Just wait here.'

They stood together in the growing gloom of evening, but Sebastian was back in the Land Rover very quickly, and he had Maggie beside him. Verity thankfully handed all responsibility over to them, letting them take Paula from her, and making no protest when Sebastian picked her up and put her into the car when she couldn't use her hands to get in. They drove to the house and she leaned her head against the window and waited patiently for several long minutes while Sebastian carried Paula up to her room before coming back to help her out.

'Verity, sweetheart. Your poor hands! What the hell happened?' he demanded fiercely, his voice bleak, angry.

Verity turned her head to look at him, her eyes staring into his face. Then she turned her head away and moved out of the supporting circle of his arm into the house. 'Paula needs a doctor,' she said dully.

'He's on his way. I phoned him before I went back for you. He lives nearby, he won't be long. Verity...'

He reached out for her, but she sat down on the nearest chair, her face very pale. 'Have you got a towel?'

He brought her one and wrapped it round her hands, then gently examined her face and gave a sigh of relief when he saw that there was no wound beneath the blood there. 'Are you going to be all right? My brave darling.' He gently stroked the hair from her face.

She shuddered uncontrollably and lifted heavy, pain-filled lids to look at him, then lowered them again. 'Yes,' she answered, her tone cold, withdrawn.

Sebastian's eyes drew into a frown. 'What happened, Verity? Paula said something about a dog.'

'It was Chivers' dog. It attacked us.'

He stared at her, appalled. 'That brute? But Chivers only keeps it as a deterrent to poachers. He never lets it loose, it's half wild. How on earth could it have got out?'

'You tell me,' Verity said harshly, her eyes again on his face.

His mouth drew into a grim line. 'You're right; I've often told Chivers we don't need a dog like that on the estate. I should have insisted that he get rid of it. But he's usually so careful about keeping it shut away.'

*'But he isn't there, is he?'*

Sebastian's eyes came swiftly up to meet hers, then were immediately hooded again, but he couldn't hide the deepening of the lines about his mouth. He hesitated, then said grimly, 'No, you're right. So someone else must have let the brute out. One of the village boys, I expect. The little devils are always up to mischief, but they've gone too far this time. I'm going to find out who was responsible and make sure they know darn well what they've done.' But his voice didn't carry conviction.

There was the sound of a car outside and Sebastian got up to let the doctor in. 'Take him up to Paula first,' she insisted.

Sebastian gave her a worried look, but did as she asked, then came hurrying back to her. 'Would you like me to help you up to your room?'

Verity looked at the blood-soaked towel and said rather faintly, 'I'm afraid you'll have to.'

He helped her to her feet, but then glanced at her face and quickly picked her up in his arms. Verity leaned against his shoulder, her body suddenly shaking as shock set in. She must have passed out for a moment, because the next thing she knew she was lying on her bed and Sebastian was gently washing her face, his eyes full of angry tenderness. It occurred to her that the village boys were in for the ticking off of their lives—if it had been the village boys. The thought brought a frown of bleakness to her eyes, and Sebastian bent to kiss her forehead and then her lips. 'Hang in there, my darling,' he said softly. 'It won't be long now.'

Almost on his words the doctor came into the room. Sebastian turned quickly towards him. 'How is Mrs Layton?' he asked sharply, his face tense.

'Badly shocked and scared, but apart from a few bruises there's no physical damage.'

'You're sure that there's no chance of her having a miscarriage? She had food poisoning only a few weeks ago, you know.'

'No,' the doctor assured him. 'As long as she rests completely for the next few days, I'm sure she'll be fine.'

Verity was watching Sebastian closely while the doctor was speaking, and saw his face gradually change, lose the almost expectant tension. But the grim look was still there around his mouth and in his eyes.

'And now let me look at you, young lady.' The doctor sat on the edge of the bed and unwound the towel. 'Yes, you have been in the wars, haven't you? I'm rather afraid you're going to need some stitches in those.'

The next half-hour wasn't at all pleasant; the doctor dressed her hands and gave her an antitetanus injection. He wanted to give her some pain-killers, too, but Verity said fretfully, 'No, I must go and see how Paula is.'

'Well, you'll have to wait, I'm afraid; I've given her something to make her sleep, although she was as bad as you and didn't want to take them until after she'd seen *you*. But I assured her that you're not badly hurt. You're young and will heal quickly. But there will be some small scars, I'm afraid.'

Verity looked down at her bandaged hands; her mind had been too full to think of scars. The doctor went away and Maggie came to help her undress and get into bed. She also brought her a glass of water to help her to swallow the pain-killers, but Verity surreptitiously dropped the pills down between the bedcovers and only pretended to take them. Even though her hands were throbbing horribly, she didn't want to dull her senses in any way. Not tonight. Looking at the small carriage clock on the bedside table, she saw that it was only seven-thirty. How long would Paula sleep? she wondered, and decided to wait until midnight before going in to her. She lay back on the pillows in the darkened room, the pain in her hands keeping her awake even if the unhappy thoughts in her mind hadn't done so.

The clock ticked on, the sound friendly in the darkness, and presently, despite everything, her eyes closed and she fell asleep.

The hand touching her made her cry out in fear, and she jerked into a sitting position, her skin prickling. 'Who is it? Who's there?' she shouted as she saw a dark figure standing over her.

'It's all right. It's me,' Sebastian's voice was quick to soothe her.

Verity reached out to the bedside lamp and fumbled with the switch, but couldn't turn it on with her bandaged hands. 'Oh, hell!'

'Here, let me.' He sat on the edge of the bed to turn on the lamp and she saw that his robe was loosely belted over pyjama trousers.

'Why are you here? What do you want?' she demanded, her voice raw with fright.

'You were having a nightmare, calling out in your sleep.'

She stared at him, only now feeling the dampness on her skin. 'Calling out? What—what was I saying?'

'I think you were reliving that damn dog attacking you. When I came in here you were shouting that you must save Paula.'

Verity visibly relaxed and Sebastian put his arm round her and drew her to him. 'My poor little love.' He brushed the damp hair back from her forehead and kissed it. 'Do your hands hurt very much?'

'No,' Verity lied on a low note.

Leaning her head against his shoulder, he gently stroked his hand down her bare arm. 'You're shaking. But it's all right, you don't have to be afraid any more; I'll stay with you till you go to sleep again.'

Tilting her head, Verity looked searchingly into his grey eyes, but Sebastian mistook her action and bent to kiss her on the lips. It was a tender kiss that only lasted a few seconds, but their eyes still held and almost immediately he kissed her again, his lips drinking deeply of hers this time. Verity gave a long, sobbing sigh against his mouth and closed her eyes, wanting to forget everything but the exquisite sensuality of his kiss, of the havoc that it played with her senses. His hand moved to cup her breast and her body quivered. His fingers lightly circled her nipple and it sprang into aching life. He parted the thin material of her nightgown to kiss her burning skin and her body arched as she moaned with pleasure.

'Verity, my darling. My sweet love. We were going to have some time together tonight, do you remember?' he murmured as he lifted his head. 'I was going to tell you how much you've come to mean to me. I'm crazy about you, but I think you know that.' He kissed her lips. 'Verity?'

Slowly she opened her eyes, a lost bleakness in their green depths. 'Please—turn off the light.'

Sebastian's brows flickered for a moment, but he did as she asked. She sighed, welcoming the dark, wanting to fool herself by believing his words, but not able to do it when she could see his face. Taking his arm from round her, Sebastian laid her back against the pillows, then lay down on the bed beside her. He caressed her again, and made love to her with words, saying softly, 'You're so beautiful, so perfect. My darling girl, I love you so.'

She turned then, and put her bandaged hands on either side of his head to kiss him in sudden fierce passion, taking him by surprise. But it lasted only a moment, and then she dropped back, her eyes pressed tightly shut as she fought to keep from crying.

'Verity!' There was delight and surprise and fascination in the word. 'What brought that on? Not that I wasn't very pleased to be on the receiving end, of course.' She didn't answer and he gently stroked her face. 'Don't tell me you're shy, my sweet. Don't you have anything to say to me? Am I to do all the running?'

She sighed unhappily and he couldn't resist putting out his hand to cover her breast as it moved beneath its silken cover. His need for an answer was forgotten then as they kissed hungrily, but when he raised his head she said, 'Sebastian, I'm so tired. What's the time?'

'Almost two in the morning, I think. I'm sorry, my darling, this isn't the right time, is it?' Gently he picked up her hands and kissed each of them. 'Your poor hands.' Pulling up the duvet, he covered her shoulders. 'Try and sleep; I'll stay here till you do.'

They lay there in the darkness with, physically, only the thickness of the covers between them, and perhaps to Sebastian that was all that was between them. But to Verity the mental gulf was like an abyss to which she could see no bottom. She stared upwards, her body tense, her heart aching.

Out of the darkness Sebastian said, 'I want you.'

'Yes.'

She could almost feel him raise his eyebrows as he gave a low, amused laugh. 'Now what are you saying yes to, I wonder?'

Verity didn't answer, she tried to make herself relax and closed her eyes, shutting out the wretched thoughts that whirled in her brain. But Sebastian lay awake beside her and it was a long time before he quietly got up from the bed, looked down at her in the faint light of dawn, and then slipped quietly from the room.

It was only after she'd heard the door latch click closed that Verity opened her eyes and drew a long breath of relief. She turned on her side, stiff from having pretended to be asleep for so long. She would give Sebastian an hour, she decided, and then go to see Paula.

It was almost full light when Verity went to the next door bedroom. Paula was asleep, but came awake quite quickly, the effects of whatever mild tranquilliser the doctor had given her almost worn off. 'Verity?' She sat up in puzzlement.

'Don't turn on the light,' Verity said urgently, keeping her voice low. 'Paula, we have to talk.'

'Now?'

'Yes.' Verity hesitated, not wanting to alarm the other girl too much, but not seeing how she could do otherwise. 'We have to leave here,' she said bluntly.

'Leave?' Paula sat up and looked into Verity's eyes, seeing such bleak unhappiness there that she immediately said, 'Yes, all right, we'll leave if you think we should, but I think you'd better tell me why. Just in case Maggie should ask me,' she added wryly.

Verity's shoulders sagged. 'There have been too many so-called accidents for them to really be accidents. I think someone is deliberately trying to make you lose the baby.'

Paula stared at her in open-mouthed surprise, then gasped, 'But that's preposterous! Who on earth would want that?'

'I should have thought that was obvious,' Verity returned grimly. 'Who stands to gain?'

The other girl's face whitened as she gazed at her. 'Surely you can't mean Sebastian? But he...' Her voice trailed off, appalled.

'I know, it's a terrible thing to think of anyone,' Verity admitted, her voice tired. 'But look at the things that have happened while we've been here. If you remember, when you got food poisoning it was

Sebastian who brought in the meal that Mrs Chivers had left ready. He was alone in the house before he came to meet us at the station and would have had plenty of opportunity to add some toadstools to the mushrooms.'

'But he had some himself,' Paula protested.

'And what better alibi than to make himself ill, too? But he made sure he had very little; he gave you most of them—because he knew how much you fancied them because you were pregnant,' Verity finished bitterly.

'Oh, but he couldn't have. He wouldn't,' Paula said in distress. 'I like him.'

'Do you?' Verity didn't say how *she* felt, instead forcing herself to say, 'And that night, he—he made sure I was out of the way by taking me outside for a spot of lovemaking. Obviously he didn't want you to get medical attention too soon.'

'Oh, Verity.' Paula touched her hand in distress.

But Verity went doggedly on. 'And yesterday I saw him in the woods, coming away from the Chivers' cottage just before the dog attacked us. Surely he must have heard us; we yelled loud enough.'

'But I remember that he came to help us from right over the other side of the grounds.'

'What are you, the devil's advocate? He was out of breath, remember? He had obviously run through the woods so that he could appear to have been working on the far side as he'd said he was going to.'

'But he ran over to us; he was bound to be out of breath. And what about the accident to you? How could that possibly be an attempt to get rid of *my* baby?' Paula said triumphantly.

'Keep your voice down.' Verity looked at her friend sadly. 'Sebastian had never seen you before we came here, and he didn't know that I was definitely coming with you because he'd been away and didn't go to the house before he drove over to see Chivers on that first day. He saw a woman leaning over the bridge and he thought it was you. That's why he ran me down.'

'But if that's so, why did he pull you back up when you were hanging from the bridge? Why didn't he just let you fall?'

'He didn't straight away,' Verity reminded her. 'He just stood there watching. But I was wearing tight jeans and a thin sweater; there was no way I could have been nearly six months pregnant. When he saw that and realised that he'd made a mistake, then he came to haul me up.'

Paula stared at her, her eyes wide and vulnerable. 'Oh, Verity, I can't believe it's true.'

'I don't *want* to believe it,' Verity said violently. 'But I have to. And we must leave here before he arranges another accident and is luckier this time.'

'Luckier?' Paula managed a weak laugh and reached out to touch Verity's face. 'You really go for him, don't you?'

'Certainly not!' Verity answered shortly.

'You always were useless at lying. Do you think Maggie is involved in this?'

'No, but she can hardly help but suspect. Didn't you see how worried she was tonight?'

'Yes,' Paula agreed. 'And when Sebastian carried me up here I heard her say to him, "This is too much. It has to be stopped," but Sebastian cut her off.' They gazed at each other until Paula suddenly put her head in her hands. 'No wonder Simon hated this place. Oh,

Verity, I'd gladly give it to them, if they want it that badly.'

'You can't, it isn't yours. And what about the baby? Are you going to meekly give away his inheritance? Some mother you are!'

Paula took her hands down and smiled. 'What would I do without you?' She sighed, accepting all Verity's arguments. 'All right, so what do we do?'

'Get away from here as soon as you feel well enough, as soon as we possibly can. The only thing is——' Verity held up her hands '—I don't think I'll be able to drive. Do you think you could drive my car?'

'Yes, but not all the way back to London, if that's what you have in mind. Don't forget I haven't driven in this country for years. And hardly at all when I was in Bahrain; they don't go much on women drivers in Arab countries.'

'Well—do you think you could drive as far as Melford with me shouting at you if you go wrong?'

'I could try,' Paula agreed cautiously.

'Great. So here's what we do. As soon as the coast is clear we'll sneak down to the garage and get my car, then we'll drive to the station at Melford and get a train up to London and go to my house. Sebastian doesn't know the address so you'll be safe there.'

'What about looking you up in the phone book?'

'No problem, I'm ex-directory.'

'What about our things?'

'We'll just have to take what we can carry.'

'I am not leaving that new evening dress behind,' Paula said on a high, unsteady note.

Verity was about to tell her not to be silly, but in time recognised that Paula needed something normal to hold on to in this suddenly mad world, even if it was only her clothes, so instead she smiled and said, 'I was afraid you'd say that. I'm definitely against leaving my things behind, too, but I don't see any other way. We can hardly ask Sebastian to carry our cases to the car for us, can we?' she said with bitter humour. 'As it is, I shall have to abandon my car at the station until I can arrange to have it collected.'

Paula reached out to touch her hand. 'All this for me. I'm sorry, Verity.'

'Don't be silly,' Verity retorted on a thick, cross note that was supposed to hide her feelings. 'Perhaps we could cram as much as we can into one case. Try and think of a way we can sneak it down to the car— I can't carry it, I'm afraid.'

'All right, I'll think of something.' Paula put her brain to work and after a few moments snapped her fingers. 'I know. In the nursery there's that toy trolley with wooden bricks in it. We could——' Her voice changed swiftly as there was a light knock on the door and Maggie came in. 'Oh, hello, Maggie, we were just talking about the nursery.'

'In that case you must both be feeling much better.' The older woman smiled at them in relief, but they both noticed the worried frown in her eyes. 'I expect you would like to have your breakfast together in here. I'll bring it up to you.'

'This isn't going to be easy,' Paula said with a sigh as soon as the door closed behind Maggie. 'I wish we could go now, this minute.'

'You need to rest first; the doctor said for a few days,' Verity said worriedly. 'But you should be all right while you're in bed here, as long as you keep the door locked. I'll stay with you as much as I pos-

sibly can, of course, but it's important that we don't
let Sebastian know that we suspect him.'

'In that case you'd better not let him near me
because I'm not very good at acting. You'll just have
to keep him occupied.'

Verity threw her an indignant look. 'Oh, thanks!'

'But you're not in any danger from him,' Paula
pointed out. 'As long as you're either with him or
with me, then I should be safe enough.'

Not in any danger? That was a laugh, Verity
thought to herself. Last night she had been in the
greatest danger of all; when he had lain beside her on
the bed and told her that he loved her, it would have
been so easy to tell him that she felt the same, to have
taken him in her arms and in her heart and let him
make love to her. It would have been easy, too, to
have told him of her suspicions so that he could have
laughed them away as he convinced her that she was
being a complete idiot. Because that was what she
wanted, more than anything else in the world: to know
him innocent and this whole thing a fantastic figment
of her imagination.

The room had grown much lighter now; Verity went
over to the window and pulled back the curtains. It
was raining. She leaned on the deep sill to look out
and saw Sebastian striding round to the garage. His
body seemed stiff with tension and there was that same
grim look on his face that she had seen yesterday. He
didn't look up and presently she saw him drive past
in the Land Rover and take the track up to the cottage.
He would be going to tell Chivers that he had to get
rid of the dog, Verity surmised. And that wasn't going
to be easy, seeing as it wasn't Chivers' fault. Would
Sebastian blame the village boys again? she wondered.

Suddenly the whole world seemed a dreary place and she was glad to turn away as Maggie came in carrying a large tray.

Maggie stayed, and they managed to make a game of Verity's having to have her food cut up and not being able to hold anything properly. It was soon obvious that Maggie wanted to know all the details of the dog's attack, showing a concerned interest that might, or might not, have been real.

Realising that she would have to tell her something, Verity gave a virtually true account, but left out seeing Sebastian, of course, and of hearing the whistle that drew the dog off.

'I didn't see very much, I'm afraid,' Paula added afterwards. 'I saw the dog coming and I started to run, but it knocked me down. Then Verity threw herself on top of me, and I'm ashamed to say I just cowered under her until the brute took himself off.'

'It was a terrible thing to happen,' Maggie said in apparent distress. 'But Sebastian has gone out now to deal with it.'

Verity left Maggie with Paula while she went into her room to dress, making a poor job of it because she couldn't wash herself properly without getting the bandages wet, and only just managing to pull up the zip of her jeans. She stayed with Paula all that morning and had lunch with her, but afterwards it became apparent that Paula wanted to rest, so Verity left her alone, first making sure that she locked the door behind her. There was no one in the sitting-room, but Verity could hear sounds coming from the kitchen. She put her head round the door, looking for Maggie, but only Mrs Chivers was there, beating at a bowl of cake mixture as if she hated it. She looked up when the door opened, and, seeing Verity, shouted, 'What do you want? This is my kitchen; if you want something, you ring the bell.'

Appalled by her rudeness, Verity stood and stared for a minute before quickly going out of the room again. Fuming, she went back to the sitting-room and tried to look through a magazine, but after a couple of minutes threw it down, too angry and tense to read. The doctor came again in the afternoon, and afterwards Paula packed the clothes they'd chosen to take with them into a large suitcase. Maggie had gone into Melford so, as soon as Mrs Chivers went home, Verity fetched the toy-brick trolley from the nursery and balanced the case on it, wheeling it quite easily across the landing, then kicked the case downstairs and wheeled it out to the garage. The trolley made rather a noise and Verity was terrified that Sebastian might arrive before she got the case into the car. But somehow she managed it and was back inside the house again within twenty minutes. But now she was so nervy and on fire to get away that the time seemed to drag by.

She was downstairs again when Sebastian came home late that afternoon. She saw him from the window and thought that he looked tired, but he glanced up and saw her and his step immediately lightened as he smiled at her and waved. Thrown into a panic at the thought of having to try and pretend that she didn't suspect him, Verity hurried into the hall to go up to Paula's room, but Sebastian got there before her. He pushed the big front door shut and strode over to her, his eyes warm, thinking that she'd come to meet him. Putting his hand on her arm, he said, 'Come into the study,' and drew her inside.

He was carrying a parcel, which he put down on the desk before pulling her into his arms and kissing her hungrily. 'I've been wanting to do that all day,' he murmured huskily when at last he raised his head.

Verity leaned against him, letting him hold her, powerless to resist, just as she had been unable to resist returning his kiss. She loved him so much; nothing would ever change that, and it was a dreadful torture to know that he could be so cruel and ruthless, was capable of going to such vicious lengths to get what he wanted—perhaps what he had come to look on as rightfully his. The thought sent a shudder of repulsion through her, but Sebastian thought it was awareness and kissed her again. Then he smiled down at her and said, 'I have a present for you.'

Turning, he picked up the parcel from his desk and gave it to her. 'Here. Open it.'

Her eyes went to his face for a moment before she reluctantly opened the cardboard box—and gave an involuntary gasp of pleasure. 'A teapot! Oh, how lovely.' Gently she removed the wrappings to completely reveal a pretty porcelain pot painted with a coloured picture of a rustic couple dancing in a wooded glade. The lid had a tiny painting on it, too, and the knob was in the shape of a flower. One look at it was enough to convince Verity of the quality of the piece, and she hardly had to look underneath to confirm her guess. 'It's Worcester, isn't it? Yes, I thought so.' She touched it caressingly, admiring the delicacy of the china and the vitality of the dancing figures. It was the sort of piece she had only ever seen in museums before, and of a much better quality than anything she had in her collection or had even aspired to own. A cracked or chipped version one day perhaps, but never anything as perfect as this. With an inward sigh, Verity gently laid the teapot back in its box.

'Don't you like it?' Sebastian asked quizzically.

'Yes, of course I do. It's perfect, the most beautiful example I've ever seen.'

'I got it from that house sale I told you about. It was today, if you remember. I wanted to take you, of course, but I knew you wouldn't want to leave Paula today, or go yourself for that matter.' Picking up her hands, he lightly kissed the tips of her fingers that showed above the bandages. 'How are they today?'

'Fine. Much better.'

'And Paula?'

Even though she'd expected the question, Verity couldn't stop herself from tensing up. Still holding her hands, Sebastian felt it and glanced swiftly at her face. In the hope that Paula was worse? Verity thought bitterly. Taking her hands from his, she turned away, not wanting to see his face as she said lightly, 'She's OK. Following the doctor's orders and resting in her room.'

Coming up behind her, Sebastian put his hands on her shoulders and kissed her neck. She closed her eyes, her chest tight with longing, and briefly raised her hands to touch his. 'Verity, my darling girl, I——'

But she stepped quickly away, afraid of what he might say, and went over to the sideboard. 'Would you like a drink?'

'No, thanks.' He looked at her keenly. 'Is something the matter, Verity?'

She swallowed, then turned to face him. 'Yes, I'm afraid there is. I know it's none of my business, but— well, Mrs Chivers was extremely rude to me today.

She actually ordered me out of the kitchen—*her* kitchen, as she called it.'

'I'm sorry. But maybe she has reason to be out of temper; you see, I ordered her and her husband to leave this morning. They have a month to find somewhere else.'

Verity's eyes widened. 'Because of the dog?'

'Partly.'

He hesitated, but before he could go on Verity said, 'Did they refuse to get rid of it?'

'Chivers was extremely reluctant.'

'Where is it now?'

'I took it to a kennels this morning; it will stay there until Chivers finds a new place. He refused point-blank to have it put down.'

'Well, that's something in his favour,' Verity surprised him by saying.

'I thought you would have been all for having it put down after what the brute did to you.'

'It wasn't the dog's fault. An animal does what it's trained to do. It's the trainer who should be punished.'

'Well, I am at least getting rid of him.' Moving to stand beside her, Sebastian slipped his arm round her waist and said, 'Where would you like to put your teapot? Up in your room or somewhere down here?'

Her face set, Verity took a step away from him. 'I'm sorry, it was very kind of you to get it for me, but I'm afraid I can't accept it.'

'Why not?' he asked, his eyes fixed on her.

'Because I can't, that's why,' she answered illogically as she turned away.

'But there must be a reason.' She was silent, the truth being the last thing she was going to tell him, and unable to think of a convincing lie. 'I meant what I said last night, Verity.'

'That you wanted me; yes, I know.'

'That I'm *in love with you*,' he corrected firmly. 'I meant the gift to commemorate yesterday for you. As a pre-engagement present, if you like,' he added deliberately.

She swung round to stare at him, her eyes wide and vulnerable, emotions chasing through them.

A rueful smile twisted Sebastian's lips. 'You seem surprised. But surely you expected this after I told you I love you?' Reaching out, he touched her hair, but she jerked away from him. His mouth tightening, Sebastian said shortly, 'What is it, Verity?'

'I can't. I—I'm sorry, but I don't want you,' she got out agitatedly.

He stared at her unbelievingly, but then she saw suspicion come into his eyes and she leapt in before he could speak, saying what she thought would most put him off. 'Look, I'm not ready to settle down yet. OK, maybe I fancy you and maybe I would have gone to bed with you if the circumstances had been different. But I'm not ready to tie myself down to one man and a couple of kids. What we did was fun, it was something to do, but I certainly didn't intend to get serious. I've got a lot of living to do yet, a lot of other men to meet and get to know. So let's leave it at that, OK?'

Sebastian's face had gone very white as he listened to her, the implications of that last sentence making him stiffen with shock. Unable to look at him or keep up the pretence any longer, Verity turned and strode out of the room, then broke into a run as she fled upstairs and rapped urgently on Paula's door. 'It's Verity. Open the door—quickly.'

She looked back down the landing, expecting Sebastian to come running after her and demand an explanation, and gave a sob of relief when Paula opened the door before he did so. Dashing into the room, she whirled round and locked the door, then looked at Paula with huge, desperate eyes. 'We have to go tonight,' she said fiercely. 'I can't stay here any longer, Paula. I just can't bear to see Sebastian again.'

# CHAPTER EIGHT

IT WAS three in the morning before they dared to make a move. Verity had eaten dinner in Paula's room and, afraid that Sebastian might try to come to her again, spent the rest of the night there. They put on coats and boots against the cold and crept out on to the landing. The house was very dark, very quiet. Paula trod on a floorboard that creaked, the sound thunderously loud to their strained nerves.

'Come on,' Verity muttered. Taking Paula's arm, she helped her down the stairs, afraid that she might fall in the dark, but they reached the hall safely and made their way through the kitchen to the back door. Reaching up, Verity unbolted it and turned the key in the lock. A draught of cold, frosty air gushed in as she pulled it open.

'Aren't you going to lock it?' Paula whispered.

'No. Come on.'

Verity left the door open because the latch closing was one more sound that might wake Sebastian, and they hurried towards the garage. The big doors were closed, but Verity went round to the side and used a key that Sebastian had given her some time ago to open a smaller door. Paula got into the driver's seat of Verity's car, adjusting the seat for her height and checking the controls, while Verity unbolted the main doors. She waited for Paula to start the engine before she opened them, knowing that the noise would be bound to reach the house. But Paula was having trouble starting the car; the battery whirred, reverberating round the garage. It stopped and Paula tried again, but the same thing happened.

Dismayed, Verity ran to the car. 'What is it?' she demanded fiercely.

'It won't start, of course,' Paula retorted.

Trying hard to control herself, Verity said as calmly as she could, 'Have you pulled the choke out?'

'Oh, no, I forgot. It was always so hot, you never had to use a choke in Bahrain.' Paula pulled out the lever and for good measure pumped the accelerator. The starter turned again, the engine almost caught, but then spluttered and died. She tried several times more, the smell of petrol filling the garage.

'For heaven's sake, Paula, can't you start a damn car?'

'Don't yell at me! I'm trying, aren't I?'

They stared at each other, realising that they were nearly shouting. 'It's no good,' Verity said. 'You've flooded the engine. We'll have to wait until it dries out.'

'No,' Paula said with stubborn firmness. 'I am not going to sit out here in the cold any longer. If the car won't start then we must go back.'

'I've told you, we have *got* to leave tonight,' Verity insisted with equal force. She looked desperately round the garage and saw the other cars. 'We'll have to take another car. Maggie's.'

'But we don't have the keys,' Paula protested. She brightened. 'But I know where Sebastian keeps the keys of the Land Rover. They're in the top drawer of his desk in the study. I saw them there when I had that talk with him about the estate.'

Verity gave her a dour look, knowing that it would mean having to go back to the house. 'All right, I'll get them.'

The walk back through the darkness alone took a great deal of courage. Once inside, she stood frozen every time there was the slightest noise, her nerves on edge, her eyes peering into the darkness. When she reached the study she had to turn the desk lamp on briefly, but luckily the drawer wasn't locked and slid open easily. She found the keys at once, and went to turn off the light when she saw the box with the teapot in it. With a small sob, she reached out to pick it up, but then drew back, switched off the light and hurried from the room. But the change to darkness blinded her for a moment, and as she went into the hall she knocked against an ornament, which fell to the floor. It landed on the carpet, but even so the noise seemed deafening in the quiet house.

Without waiting to see if it had wakened anyone, Verity fled to the garage and thrust the keys in Paula's hands. 'Here, and remember the choke this time.' She heaved the suitcase out of her own car, wincing as the effort pulled at the stitches in her hands, and somehow got it into the back of the Land Rover. 'Ready?'

The blessed diesel engine fired first time and Paula gave her a grin as the noise filled the garage. 'Yes.'

Verity ran to the wooden doors and pushed them open—but as she glanced at the house saw that lights were coming on in the rooms as someone ran through it. 'Quickly, he's coming.' She jumped into the passenger seat and Paula drove out of the garage, but oh, so slowly. 'Can't you go any faster?' Verity demanded in a panic.

'The engine is still cold; I don't want to stall it. And I'm not sure which gear I'm in.'

Looking over her shoulder, Verity saw a light go on in the kitchen, and then Sebastian ran out of the back door. He stood for a moment, poised in the shaft of light, wearing only a tracksuit that he must have hurriedly pulled on. Seeing the Land Rover, he began to run towards it, and for a terrifying moment Verity thought that he was going to catch them up. 'Go faster!' she screamed at Paula. 'He's coming.'

The vehicle jerked as Paula's foot slipped off the pedal in fright, and Sebastian got close enough to see Verity. He hesitated for barely a second and then reached out for the door-handle, his furious eyes glaring into her terrified ones. But then Paula found the accelerator again and they shot forward, leaving him behind.

'Oh, hell, oh, hell!' Verity found that she was babbling with fright.

'It's all right, he's gone,' Paula said reassuringly. She headed down the drive, but as they approached the cattle-grid she fiddled with the light switches and plunged them into sudden darkness. Hastily she braked to a stop.

'What are you *doing*?' Verity shrieked.

'Trying to put the headlights on main beam.'

'You've turned them off!'

Paula flicked the switch the right way and the headlights cut through the night. She drove on, but slowed right down for the cattle-grid, never having driven over one before. Still apprehensive, Verity twisted round to look through the back window—and nearly died. Another pair of headlights was just emerging from the garage and coming after them!

'D-don't panic,' she said in a voice that was raw with fright, 'but please try and go faster.'

Paula glanced in the driving mirror and said, 'Oh, I see.' Then, 'But he's going the other way, towards the woods.'

Puzzled, they watched the other lights flickering through the trees, until they both realised what Sebastian was doing at the same moment. 'He's trying to cut us off!' Paula exclaimed.

'And we still have to open the gates. Oh, Paula, *hurry*!'

They raced on, but the car was going even faster, driven at a breakneck and dangerous speed for that muddy, unmade-up track.

'We're not going to make it!' Paula wailed. She put her foot down, but the car burst out of the woods and shot across the piece of open ground towards the driveway near the gates.

'That's my car!' Verity exclaimed. 'He must have got it going. But how did he——?' She looked at Paula. 'Did you leave the keys in it?'

But there was no time for recriminations. They expected Sebastian to block the gates, but he drove right past them and then turned the car in a sweeping half-circle.

'What's he doing?' Paula cried. And then, with real fear in her voice. 'Verity, he's coming straight at us!'

'He wants us to pull off the drive and crash. Don't you see? It will be just another accident! Stop, Paula, this Land Rover is tougher than my car.'

Paula jerked on the handbrake and they threw their arms round each other in terror, their eyes fixed on the windscreen as the other headlights came hurtling down the drive at them. But at what seemed the last moment the lights swerved off to the right and sped past.

It was Paula who reacted first; she immediately began to drive again and went tearing up to the gates. 'Quick, get out and open them.'

But Verity was staring out of the rear window. 'Oh, Paula, I think he's crashed.'

'What?'

'The lights suddenly disappeared. I think Sebastian hit the corner of the bridge and went into the river.'

'He couldn't have! And even if he did it serves him damn well right. Come on, Verity, open the gates.'

Verity obeyed her, jumping out and running to swing the big metal gates open, but her eyes probed the darkness, trying to see through the trees to the river. 'Get in, get in!' Paula called impatiently. Verity did so, and Paula drove through the gates and turned to the left, towards Melford. 'We made it!' Paula exulted. 'Oh, lord, I was really scared back there.'

She went on talking excitedly, but Verity sat silently beside her, and after they'd gone about half a mile Verity suddenly said urgently, 'Paula, stop the Land Rover.'

'What?'

'I have to go back and make sure Sebastian didn't crash. He might be hurt.'

'But you can't!' Paula said in consternation. 'We're trying to get away from him. That's what this is all about, isn't it?'

'I'm sorry, I have to. Stop, *please*.'

Paula reluctantly drew into the side, but said firmly, 'I'm not going to turn round and go back there, Verity; we had enough trouble getting away.'

'No, it's all right. I'll go alone. Look, you go on to Melford. Go to that hotel near the station and book a room. You'll be safe enough there.'

'What about you?'

'I'll be OK. Don't worry about me. I'll just find out what happened and then I'll get the first bus in.' She saw Paula's face and said on a sudden fierce note, 'I *have* to go back and make sure, Paula. I can't just drive away when he might be hurt.' She jumped out of the car and watched to make sure Paula pulled away safely, then turned and began to run back down the road as fast as she could.

It seemed an agonisingly long way. By the time Verity came to the river her heart was thudding and her panting breath forming little clouds of steam in the cold air. She paused on the edge of the steep bank, hardly daring to look down, but then gave a cry of dread as she saw that she was right: the car *had* crashed. It was lying at an angle, the front of it in the river, blocking the flow so that a wide pool had gathered around it. The water was making loud gurgling sounds as it sought to pass, as if angry that its peaceful progress should have been so violently interrupted. The night wasn't so dark now, and Verity could see that the driver's side was almost underwater, but the passenger door was open. Had he managed to get out—or had the door come open in the crash?

There was only one way to find out. Verity took off her coat and plunged into the water, gasping as the icy cold hit her. She peered in the windows of the car, trying to see if Sebastian was inside, but it was too dark to be sure. Her teeth chattering violently, she waded round to the other side and pushed the door open wider. 'Sebastian?' There was no answer, and in an agony of fear she climbed into the car and groped around the driver's seat. She searched frantically for him, calling his name, terrified that he might have already drowned. But her cold, numb hands found no body trapped in the seat or slumped on the floor. He must have got out, she thought on a great wave of relief that was so overwhelming it made her feel dizzy.

Turning, Verity got hold of the door-frame and somehow managed to heave herself out, sliding down into the water as her foot slipped, and giving a yelp of pain as she caught her leg on a piece of broken glass. A sound startled her and she looked wildly round. 'Who is it?' It came again, unmistakably a human voice, giving a low moan. 'Sebastian!' She waded as fast as she could through the freezing water to where she could make out the darker shadow of a clump of reeds a few feet away. He was there! Almost hidden in the reeds, and up to his shoulders in the water.

'Sebastian? Are you all right?' But his only answer was another low moan.

Putting her arms under his, Verity pulled him through the reeds and then, struggling and gasping, her feet constantly slipping from under her on the muddy slope, she somehow managed to drag him up the bank. Taking a deep, panting breath, Verity tilted his head back and placed her mouth over his, petrified that he might be dying, and trying to put life back into his body. But it was only a few moments before he groaned and opened his eyes. 'Verity?'

'Yes, I'm here. You're all right. Don't worry.'

He coughed. 'The car—the brakes.' He tried to sit up, but then fell back again, his body shaking with cold.

Remembering her coat, Verity ran back over the bridge to find it, stumbling, her boots full of water. When she got back Sebastian was struggling to get to his feet, but was completely disorientated and had slipped part way down the bank. 'Oh, no!' She pulled him back and wrapped her coat round him as he fell to his knees, his legs too numbed by cold to carry him. 'Stay here. Don't try to move. I'm going to get help, I won't be long.'

'Verity.' He tried to catch hold of her arm.

With a little sob, she put her hands on either side of his face and gave him a fierce kiss, passionate but brief, then turned and ran for the house.

She had seen the flash of a torch near the garage and called out, 'Maggie! Maggie!', but her teeth were chattering so much that the sound came out as a thin, uneven wail.

There was fear in Maggie's voice as she called sharply, 'Who's there? Verity? Is that you?' She ran forward, a coat pulled over her nightdress. 'What on earth's happening? There's no one in the house. Do you know where Sebastian is?'

'Yes. He—he's had an accident. But he's all right. He's by the river. We must——' But Maggie had gone, running across the grass to find her son.

Verity hesitated, then ran into the house and called for an ambulance before grabbing up the whisky decanter and some travelling rugs from the chest in the hall. Her head swimming with the cold from her wet clothes and from running so much, she tore back to Sebastian and Maggie, but had hardly thrust the whisky into Maggie's hands when a pair of headlights pierced the deep grey of the sky as a car turned into the drive.

'That will be the police!' Maggie exclaimed. 'I rang them earlier. Go and stop them. Bring them here.'

With a groaning gasp, Verity somehow staggered on to the driveway and held up her hands, unable to find the strength to even look up and see if they were going to stop. The headlights reached her, grew stronger, and finally came to a dazzling halt a few yards away. A policeman got out and she pointed feebly over at the others, then dropped to her knees in the road, too exhausted to move.

When the ambulance came it was almost a toss-up who they took away, but Verity insisted on staying behind while Maggie went with Sebastian. Although he hadn't wanted to go either; she had heard him arguing that he was all right, but did it in so weak a voice that no one took any notice of him. Another police car came with a policewoman in it who helped Verity up to her room and into a hot shower. She stood there under the water for a long time, thinking that she would never feel warm again, but the shivers slowly died away and she came out to towel herself dry and put on some of the clothes that she'd left behind.

The police were waiting for her in the sitting-room when she came down, wanting to know what had happened.

'It—it was an accident,' she lied. 'Sebastian—Mr Kent was driving home when he skidded into the river.'

The policeman gave her an old-fashioned look. 'At that hour in the morning? I think I should tell you,

Miss Mitchell, that there was a phone call while you were upstairs. From a Mrs Layton.'

'Maggie?' Verity got nervously to her feet. 'Is it Sebastian? Is he—is he . . .?'

'No, the call was from a Mrs Paula Layton. She was evidently very worried because you hadn't followed her to Melford. She had quite an interesting story to tell us about some suspicious accidents that have been happening here.' He eyed Verity keenly as the last vestige of returning colour drained from her face. 'Would you have anything to add to what she's told us?'

The policewoman came in with a hot milk drink laced with brandy for her. Verity took it awkwardly and sat down. 'No,' she answered in a voice they could hardly hear. 'I have nothing to add.'

Paula had booked them into a two-bedroomed suite at the hotel. The police dropped Verity off in Melford at about nine in the morning, after trying to persuade and threaten her into making a statement which she steadfastly refused to give. She had spoken to Paula on the phone earlier, though, and wasn't surprised to find her friend fast asleep in bed when she peeped into her room. Verity stripped off her clothes and climbed into bed, too worn out to search for a nightdress. But she had gone past physical exhaustion and lay awake for a long time.

It was over now, she knew that. Whatever the outcome there would be no future for her with Sebastian. She wondered if there would be a trial and Sebastian would be sent to prison now that Paula had told the police everything. She felt terribly sad. She had hoped to keep the whole thing hushed up, and probably would have succeeded if Sebastian hadn't

come after them in her car. Which was still stuck in
the river and would probably be a write-off, she realised. Thinking of the car made her remember what
Sebastian had said when he'd come round. Something about the brakes. She frowned, puzzled that he
should say that, but her brain was too numb and tired
and she at last fell asleep.

'Verity, wake up.'

Paula was shaking her shoulder, but it was some
moments before Verity reluctantly came awake. 'What
is it?' She sat up and looked around, momentarily
bewildered by her surroundings and the fact that she
was quite naked. But then reality came flooding back
and she looked at Paula in alarm.

'The police are here again,' Paula told her. 'And
they've brought Sebastian with them.'

'What?' Verity stared at her unbelievingly.

'It seems they have something to tell us, but
Sebastian is insisting that you be there.'

'OK, I'll—I'll get dressed. Are you all right?'

'Yes. I wonder why they brought Sebastian here. I
nearly died when I opened the door and saw him.'

Paula went on talking nervously while Verity
dressed, pulling on trousers and a sweater and
brushing her hair into a gleaming halo around her
head. She glanced into the mirror and was startled by
the pale tautness of her face and the dark shadows
around her eyes. Her hand went out to her make-up
bag, but Paula, her voice impatient, said, 'Oh, don't
bother with that; I want to find out why they're here.
I'm sure they have something unpleasant to tell us.'

'All right. I'm ready, then.'

Paula walked ahead of her into the sitting-room of
the suite. It was a small room and the three people

already there seemed to fill it. The police inspector whom Verity had seen last night was sitting in an armchair, his face weary, and a policewoman, a different one this time, was sitting on an upright chair near the door. The inspector politely got to his feet as they came in, but Verity's eyes went straight to the window where Sebastian was standing, looking out. He turned slowly and Verity shrivelled up at the cold bitterness in his eyes when they met hers.

She stood still in the doorway, frozen by his anger, until the policeman said, 'Perhaps you would care to sit down, Miss Mitchell?'

'N-no, thanks. I'll stand.'

Paula sat down on the edge of the other armchair, her fingers picking nervously at the arms, her eyes darting every other moment at Sebastian. But Verity turned so that her back was towards him, so that she didn't have to look into his eyes.

The inspector, taking control naturally, said to Paula, 'We have conducted enquiries into the complaint you made, Mrs Layton, and I have to tell you that an arrest has now been made.' At this Paula and Verity glanced quickly at each other, but neither of them could look at Sebastian. 'However,' the policeman went on, 'when I interviewed Mr Kent, here, at the hospital, he had an entirely different version of the story to tell me, and it was acting on his information that the arrest was made.'

Paula looked at him in bewilderment. 'I'm sorry, I don't understand. Are you saying that you've arrested someone else, not Sebastian?'

'Yes, Mrs Layton, that's exactly what I'm saying.'

For a moment Verity couldn't believe it, couldn't take it in. She stared at the inspector, then swung round to Sebastian, a great light of hope and happiness filling her face. He looked at her sardonically, then pointedly turned his head away.

Shattered, it was a few moments before she heard the inspector as he went on, 'It seems that Mr Kent also suspected that what had happened to you hadn't been accidental, but he had a good idea who was responsible, so acting on his information we interviewed this person, and we have now obtained a full confession.'

'But who?' Paula demanded in bewildered distress. 'Who could possibly hate me so much that they would try and kill my baby?'

The inspector stood up, followed like an automaton by the policewoman. 'As to that, Mrs Layton, I think it would be better if Mr Kent told you himself. I'm merely here at his request to assure you that he was in no way responsible for the incidents.' He held out his hand to her and Paula automatically shook it. 'Goodbye, Mrs Layton, Miss Mitchell.' He ran a hand over his face. 'I'm going home to get some sleep.' He glanced at Sebastian. 'You're sure you wouldn't like the WPC here to stay?' And he indicated the waiting policewoman.

Sebastian shook his head and they left, leaving the room suddenly alive with tension. Paula got to her feet and turned to Sebastian, her eyes wide with apprehension. 'What have you got to tell me? What *is* all this?'

Ignoring Verity, Sebastian went over to Paula and put his hand on her arm in a comforting gesture, a look of angry concern on his face. 'I'm sorry, Paula. I'd hoped to save you this, but now I have no choice but to tell you.' He paused, as if reluctant to begin, then said heavily, 'I don't suppose Simon ever told you why he quarrelled with his father?' Paula shook her head, her eyes fixed on his face. 'Well, I'm afraid it was because of a girl. Her name was Maxine Chivers.'

'Chivers? You mean she was related to the Chiverses who work at the house?'

Sebastian nodded, but Verity was already way ahead of Paula and felt no surprise when Sebastian said, 'Yes. She's their daughter. She's the girl Verity met when she was with me in Melford a few weeks ago.' He paused, but when Paula didn't say anything, just gazed at him in growing alarm, he went on quickly, 'Simon came home from university one summer and— well, I'm afraid he fell for the girl's rather too obvious attractions. He was at a susceptible age and she set out to seduce him. And succeeded. My mother and stepfather had gone for a cruise that year and were away most of the summer, and I was away on business quite a lot, too, so there was no one really to stop what was going on until it was too late.'

'How do you mean, "too late"?' Paula sat down in the chair and spoke in a suddenly toneless voice.

'Maxine got pregnant,' Sebastian said bluntly, adding, 'I'm quite sure that that was what she intended all along. She was older than Simon, and, if her reputation in the area was true, far more experienced. She knew that Simon was his father's heir and she saw the opportunity to have a part of that.'

'You're not saying that Simon married her?' Paula said in an appalled voice.

'No.' Sebastian hastened to reassure her. 'Luckily the shock of finding out that she was pregnant and her demands that he marry her at once without waiting for his father to come home jolted him out of the infatuation and Simon came to me. I sorted things out,' he explained briefly.

Paula looked very pale. Verity went over to her and knelt down beside her chair. 'Are you OK? You don't have to listen to any more of this now if you don't want to, you know.'

'No, I have to know it all. Go on, Sebastian, tell me what happened. Why has this girl attacked me?'

'The child was definitely Simon's, I'm afraid. I checked on that first of all,' Sebastian told her. 'Simon's father had to be told, of course, and there was one hell of a row. Simon was sent to business school in America, and Maxine, when she realised that she'd lost out on him marrying her, agreed to have the child adopted—for a large sum of money, of course.' His voice was dry, sardonic, and Verity knew now why he had treated the girl with such contempt when they had met her in the park that day.

'She left the area,' Sebastian went on. 'That was part of the deal, but we felt obliged to keep on the Chiverses; it was hardly their fault, although they blamed Simon. And Maxine evidently still felt that she'd been cheated, that she should have been the mistress at Layton House and her child the heir. When the police interviewed her, they found that she was into drugs, which heightened her feelings of vindictiveness. Unfortunately your arrival here coincided with a visit she made to her parents, and when she learned that you were pregnant all her spite turned against you.' Sebastian paused, shrugged his shoulders. 'I wouldn't like to even guess what went on in her mind, but the police believe that part of it was that she wanted to be revenged on me for sending

Simon away. They think she got the idea for the attacks on you after I'd accidentally knocked Verity off the bridge.'

Verity looked at him quickly when he mentioned her name, but Sebastian kept his eyes firmly on Paula as he continued, 'Maxine found out everything that was going on in the house from her mother, of course. On the night when you got food poisoning, she prepared the meal, knowing that Maggie was out and I would be blamed if anyone suspected. Just as I was,' he added with heavy implication. 'That's why she turned the radiophone on, so that Maggie wouldn't find out it was her and not her mother, if she rang. And it was she who let the dog loose, of course.'

Paula raised her eyes to meet his. 'But Verity saw you in the woods near the cottage, hurrying away just before the dog attacked us.'

'Yes, so the police told me. But I'd seen Maxine near the bridge so I went over there and told her to clear out. I was afraid she might try and talk to you, tell you about Simon.' Again he put his hand on Paula's shoulder. 'I didn't want you to be upset after you'd been so ill. She said she had a right to visit her parents, and was damn rude about it, so I insisted on her going back to the cottage, and went with her to make sure she did. Then I went over to the other side of the grounds to mark the trees.'

'You got there very quickly.'

He nodded. 'Yes, I was fuming with anger.' He gave an exasperated sigh. 'Just as I was the day you arrived at Layton House. I'd found out from Mother that Maxine was back in the area after I'd expressly told her parents to make sure she stayed away. And

I was on my way to tell them that if she made any trouble they would have to leave.'

'No wonder they were so surly,' Paula commented sadly. She looked at Sebastian. 'When did you realise that it was her?'

'Not until she let the dog loose, I'm afraid. We believed Mrs Chivers about the mushrooms. But no one but Maxine could have turned the dog loose. And I gather it was whistled off—only she could have done that, too. After that I told Chivers they had to go. Maxine had taken herself off, though, and I hoped we'd seen the last of her, and I wouldn't have to tell you about Simon.' He straightened up, his face tightening. 'But Chivers saw your suitcase in Verity's car and guessed that you were planning to leave. I can only think he told his wife, who couldn't resist passing the news on to Maxine by phone. Anyway, Maxine came back and tampered with the brakes of the car. The police found that out when they hauled it out of the river this morning. That's why it wouldn't stop when I tried to block you at the gates last night.'

'And why you swerved to avoid us and went into the river,' Verity said slowly.

Turning his head to look directly at her, Sebastian said, 'Quite,' in a scathingly remote tone.

'She could have killed us,' Paula said in an appalled voice. She stood up. 'I'm sorry, Sebastian, but I don't think I can take any more of this at the moment.' She took his hand. 'And I'm so sorry that we ever doubted you.'

He nodded briefly. 'I'll leave you, then, and let you rest.'

'Oh, no, please don't go. As it's safe now, I'd very much like to go back to the house.' She smiled, her hand still in his. 'I'm afraid we stole your Land Rover, but I really don't feel up to driving it back. Would you be very kind and drive us home?'

'Yes, of course.' He looked as if he was going to say something else, but changed his mind when Paula reached up and kissed him.

'That's for trying so hard to protect poor Simon,' she said huskily, then turned and went into her room.

Paula always did know how to make a good exit, Verity thought indulgently. She turned to Sebastian, but he had gone to the window again and stood looking moodily out, his shoulders tense. 'Sebastian?' she said tentatively.

'Well?' he returned shortly, without turning round.

Her face hardening at his tone, Verity gazed at his back for a moment and then walked over to stand beside him. 'What a riveting view!' she exclaimed mockingly. 'I've never seen such beautiful roof-tops and railway lines.' He turned his head to glare at her and she said shortly, 'Don't expect me to apologise for suspecting you, Sebastian, because I'm not going to. And I'm not going to beg your forgiveness, either, because I'm not the grovelling type. Under the circumstances I was perfectly justified in trying to get Paula away from you.'

Sebastian rounded on her angrily. 'Couldn't you have come to me, told me of your suspicions?'

'No, of course not,' Verity returned curtly. 'How could I?'

'You could have *trusted* me.' And there was raw pain in his voice.

'Yes, *I* could have trusted you—but I didn't dare trust Paula to you! Can't you see that? Everything pointed to you. And I hardly knew you; how was I to know that you wouldn't do anything to get Layton House for yourself? After all, it was your home and Paula was just——'

'My home?' Sebastian bit out with a harsh laugh. 'Didn't it ever occur to you that my mother and I might resent being used by Simon as his servants, just unpaid caretakers, stuck with that millstone of a house? James Gillis asked Mother to marry him years ago, but she felt that she couldn't leave Layton House until Simon came home and took it over. But Simon, of course, was always too busy to take on his responsibilities, and just left it all to us. He always was damn thoughtless!' he added forcefully.

'No,' Verity admitted hollowly, 'that never occurred to me. I thought you must love the place.'

'So you naturally assumed that I would be willing to go to any lengths to get it,' Sebastian said scathingly. 'If I'd wanted the damn estate that badly I could always have offered to lease it from Paula, couldn't I? Or didn't anything as simple as that occur to you, either? You just naturally believed the worst of me.' He glared at her, his eyes contemptuous. 'So much for love!'

Verity bit her lip, realising how much she had hurt him. She wanted to throw herself in his arms and tell him she was sorry, convince him of how wretched she felt, but she instinctively knew that that wasn't the way to handle it, so instead her chin came up and she said, 'I never said that I was in love with you.'

Sebastian had turned back to the window, but now he swung round, his eyes flying to meet hers, and she saw by the sudden fear in them that he still cared.

'But I am—very much,' she said softly. 'In my heart I don't think I ever believed that you could do anything so dreadful, but I just couldn't take the chance—not when Paula's life and that of her child were at stake. I wanted to trust you—so much.' She paused and said with difficulty, 'I think the worst moments of my life were when you came down the drive straight at us...' Her voice had grown very husky and she bit her lip. 'I thought that if you hit us, then you must be mad and you had done those terrible things. But you swerved and went into the river and nearly drowned.'

She raised tear-filled eyes to meet his and saw that the tension had gone from his face. Slowly he reached out and put his hands on her arms. 'So I had to nearly get killed before you believed I was innocent, did I?'

Verity gave him a misty, tremulous smile. 'Yes, I'm afraid you did.'

'I don't remember very much about that, but you were there, weren't you? I can remember being terribly cold and wet and you pulling and shouting at me.' He grinned suddenly, his smile tearing at her heart, and his hands tightened. 'But there is something I do remember, though. You kissed me. More than once.'

'Nonsense,' Verity smiled back. 'I was giving you the kiss of life, that's all.'

Sebastian's eyes darkened. 'Then would you mind doing it again—for the rest of my life?'

Verity gasped, not expecting so much, so soon, but then she went joyfully into his arms. 'Oh, yes! Oh, Sebastian, I love you so much.'

'So my ploy worked.' Paula's voice made them reluctantly turn their heads after a long, deeply passionate embrace, although Sebastian kept his arms possessively round Verity as if he never wanted to let her go. 'I knew if I left you two alone together every-thing would work out,' Paula went on with satis-faction. 'But you've got to promise not to get married until after the baby is born so that I can be a matron of honour.'

'You were listening,' Verity said accusingly.

'Of course. You didn't want me to come in too soon, did you?' And, when they both burst into laughter, 'Thank goodness that's settled. Now can we please have something to eat? I'm starving!'

Paula's baby was born on Christmas morning. It was a boy, and she called him Adam.

'So we're to be godparents,' Sebastian remarked as he and Verity walked across the mist-laden lawns later that day. They stopped near the hollow where the oak had once stood, and Sebastian dug a hole in which they planted a new sapling, a young tree that would grow with the infant lord of the manor.

Verity watched him, looking at the frail branches of the tree made into delicate lace by the frost. 'I hope it grows after such a poor start.'

'It will grow, we'll see to that,' Sebastian answered confidently. He straightened up and drew her close against his side, his arm round her waist. 'We'll have to try and make up to the child for not having a father.'

'Somehow I don't think that will be necessary,' re-marked Verity. Sebastian raised his eyebrows, and she added, 'Paula informed me a few days ago that she had decided to marry Piers in a year or so.'

'Really?' Sebastian's eyes widened in surprise. 'When did all that happen? We've hardly seen Piers since he's been decorating his Arabian palace.'

'As a matter of fact, I don't think he knows yet. It's something that Paula has decided. But it seems that he asked Paula to marry him before ever she met Simon, but she turned him down because she wasn't in love with him.'

'And she is now?'

'No.' Verity shook her head, her eyes a little sad. 'But she feels that she had romance with Simon and now she's ready to settle for companionship.'

'Piers will teach her to love him, though,' Sebastian said confidently.

'Yes.' Verity nodded in satisfaction. 'Yes, I think he will.'

They came to the bridge and paused to look down at the cold grey water. Verity shivered. 'I'm glad we'll be leaving here soon. This place has so many bad memories.'

'But so many wonderful ones, too,' Sebastian reminded her. 'Wasn't it here, for instance, that we first kissed? Like this.'

Taking her in his arms, he looked lovingly into her face for a moment, then kissed her with the deep, tender possession of a man very much in love. And as Verity returned his kiss she forgot the dark memories of the past, and thought only of their bright, shining future together.

# Just answer these simple questions for your FREE book

1 **Who is your favourite author?** _____

2 **The last romance you read** *(apart from this one)* was? _____

3 **How many Mills & Boon Romances have you bought in the last 6 months?** _____

4 **How did you first hear about Mills & Boon?** *(Tick one)*
❏ Friend   ❏ Television   ❏ Magazines or newspapers
❏ Saw them in the shops   ❏ Received a mailing
❏ other *(please describe)* _____

5 **Where did you get this book?**

_____

6 **Which age group are you in?**
❏ Under 24   ❏ 25-34   ❏ 35-44
❏ 45-54   ❏ 55-64   ❏ Over 65

7 **After you read your Mills & Boon novels, what do you do with them?**
❏ Keep them   ❏ Give them away
❏ Lend them to friends
❏ Other *(Please describe)*
_____
_____

8 **What do you like about Mills & Boon Romances?**

_____

9 **Are you a Mills & Boon subscriber?**   ❏ Yes   ❏ No

---

*Fill in your name and address, put this page in an envelope and post TODAY to:* **Mills & Boon Reader Survey, FREEPOST, P.O. Box 236, Croydon, Surrey. CR9 9EL**

**NO STAMP NEEDED**

Name (Mrs. / Miss. / Ms. / Mr.) _____

Address _____

_____

_____ Postcode _____

**mps** MAILING PREFERENCE SERVICE   You may be mailed with offers as a result of this questionnaire

PWQ1